United States
Activity Book

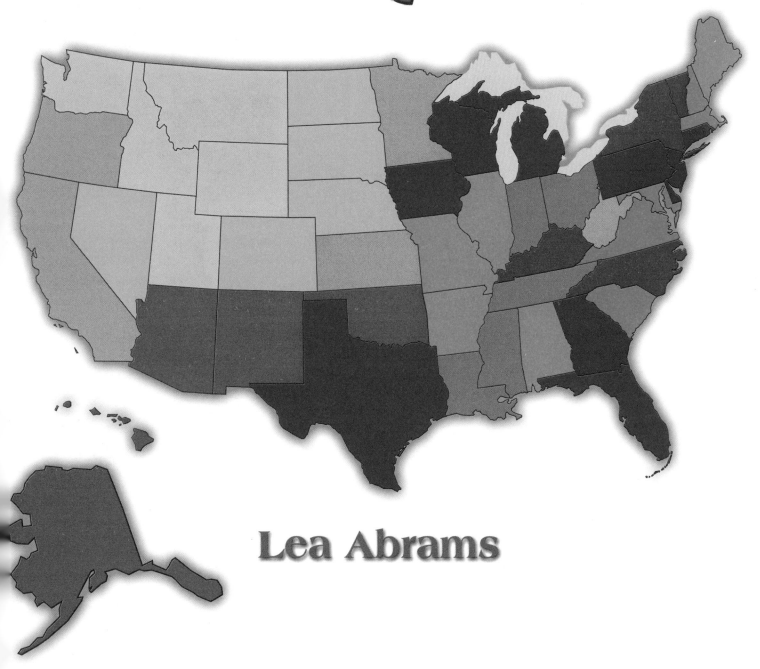

Lea Abrams

FRIEDMAN/FAIRFAX
PUBLISHERS

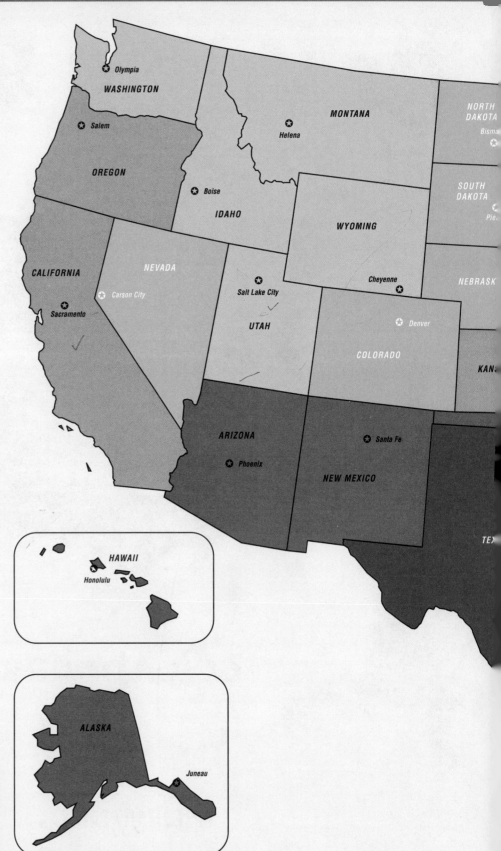

WASHINGTON
★ Olympia

★ Salem
OREGON

MONTANA
★ Helena

NORTH DAKOTA
Bisma
☆

IDAHO
★ Boise

WYOMING

SOUTH DAKOTA
Pie.
☆

CALIFORNIA

NEVADA
☆ Carson City

★ Sacramento

Salt Lake City
☆

UTAH

Cheyenne
☆

COLORADO
☆ Denver

NEBRASK

KAN

ARIZONA
☆ Phoenix

Santa Fe
☆

NEW MEXICO

TE

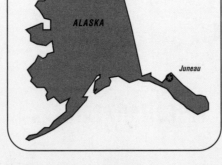

HAWAII
Honolulu

ALASKA
Juneau

merica and Its Capitals

MINNESOTA

WISCONSIN

St. Paul

Madison

MICHIGAN

MAINE

Augusta

Montpelier

VERMONT

NEW HAMPSHIRE
MASSACHUSETTS

Concord

Albany

Boston
Providence

NEW YORK

RHODE ISLAND
CONNECTICUT

Hartford

IOWA

Lansing

Des Moines

ILLINOIS

OHIO

PENNSYLVANIA

Harrisburg

Trenton

NEW JERSEY

coln

INDIANA

Columbus

Dover

MISSOURI

Springfield

Indianapolis

WEST
VIRGINIA

Annapolis

DELAWARE
MARYLAND

Topeka

Jefferson City

Frankfort

Charleston

Washington
D.C.

Richmond

KENTUCKY

VIRGINIA

Nashville

Raleigh

lahoma City

ARKANSAS

TENNESSEE

NORTH CAROLINA

OKLAHOMA

Little Rock

SOUTH CAROLINA

Columbia

MISSISSIPPI

Atlanta

Montgomery

GEORGIA

LOUISIANA

Jackson

ALABAMA

Austin

Baton Rouge

Tallahassee

FLORIDA

1999 2000 2001 2002 2003 2004 2005 2006 2007 2008

Do you know which state has the coldest recorded temperature, or tallest mountain? How about where the most battles of the Revolutionary War were fought? Maybe you've got the answers to *these* questions, but there are probably tons of other fun facts you're missing out on—like where the cheeseburger was first invented, which city has a volcano within its limits, or which state is home to the skeleton of a pre-historic man!

Delaware Congressman Michael Castle might not have had these exact pieces of trivia in mind when he introduced the bill for the special state coins, but he *was* hoping the program would teach us all a little more about the history of the states. His plan was to give each state its own quarter; since we see coins all the time, we'd kind of *have* to notice the designs and pick up some new knowledge. Why was the quarter chosen? Duh—it's the largest one!

President Bill Clinton made the idea official on December 1, 1997, when he signed The 50 States Commemorative Coin Program Act. Now it's in the hands of the U.S. Mint, the government organization responsible for making money. Since 1999, they have been releasing a new design every ten weeks, and they will continue to do so until 2008 when each state's quarter is completed. By the way, anytime you get a state quarter in your hands, hold onto it—because as soon as the U.S. Mint moves on to a new state, they stop making the previous one's quarter.

How did they decide the order in which to make the quarters? Simple— it's based on the order in which the states became a part of the United States. The process to choose the designs is a little more complicated, though. First, each state's governor has to appoint a special committee to propose ideas, then the governor submits the designs to the Secretary of the Treasury to be signed off on, and *then* the governor selects the final winning image. Whew! The map in the front of this book is color coded for the release date of each state's quarter. New York, for instance, is red— check the bottom of the map and you'll see that the red states' quarters will be out in 2001.

Since the point of the quarter program is to help everyone pick up some new info about America, why don't you get started by flipping through this book? We guarantee you'll find out some things you *never* knew about your country!

Alabama

DATE OF INDUCTION:
December 14, 1819

STATE CAPITAL: Montgomery

STATE TREE: Southern pine
(AKA Longleaf yellow pine)

STATE FLOWER: Camellia

STATE BIRD: Yellowhammer

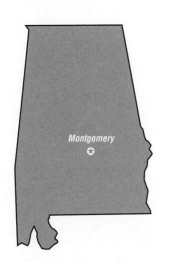

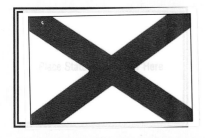

Located in the Deep South, Alabama has been the site of all kinds of exciting advances! NASA scientists developed the first rocket to send people to the moon at the Alabama Space and Rocket center in Huntsville. And in 1955, Rosa Parks made history in Montgomery when she refused to sit in the African-American section in the back of the bus, igniting a widespread bus boycott that sparked the Civil Rights movement. Helen Keller, born here in 1880, was an inspiration to everyone with all she accomplished despite being blind, deaf, *and* mute. And Alabama natives have taken the world of sports by storm. Hank Aaron and Willie Mays both grew up to become record-setting Hall of Fame baseball players, while track star Jesse Owens earned four gold medals at the 1936 Olympics in Berlin!

How Alabama Got Its Name

The name is believed to have come from two Choctaw words, *alba* and *amo,* meaning "plant-gatherer." Alabama is also known as the Yellowhammer State, the Camellia State, and the Heart of Dixie.

Historic Sites

- Civil Rights Memorial in Montgomery, designed by architect Maya Lin

- Old North Hull Street Historic District

State Trivia

- Along with being the capital of Alabama, Montgomery was also the capital and birthplace of the Confederate States of America. In fact, the Confederate flag was designed and first flown in Alabama, in 1861.

- Scientist George Washington Carver discovered three hundred new uses for the peanut in Alabama, which is probably why the state is now home to the National Peanut Festival every October. Pretty nutty!

- October must be a busy month here—it's also the time of the Tale Telling Festival, held in Selma. Got any good ones to share?

- The world's first electric trolley system began operating in Montgomery in 1886.

- Take a trip to Russel Cave and see the place where the skeleton of a pre-historic man was found!

Alaska

DATE OF STATEHOOD:
January 3, 1959

STATE CAPITAL: Juneau

STATE TREE: Sitka spruce

STATE FLOWER: Wild forget-me-not

STATE BIRD: Willow ptarmigan

When U.S. Secretary of State William Seward purchased Alaska in 1867 for roughly two cents an acre, people called it "Seward's Folly" because they believed the state was worthless. Some folly! His faith was proved right when both gold *and* oil—two of the most valuable resources in existence—were discovered here. The coldest and largest state in America, Alaska also has our country's highest point (Mt. Denali, also known as Mt. McKinley), westernmost point (Cape Wrangell), and northernmost point (Point Barrow). Alaska residents don't have to pay any income tax, because the state makes so much money from its oil fields. They also enjoy especially large fruits and vegetables, since all the extra sunlight helps the produce grow bigger. In the summer, the sun shines almost twenty-four hours a day—which is how Alaska earned its nickname, the Land of the Midnight Sun.

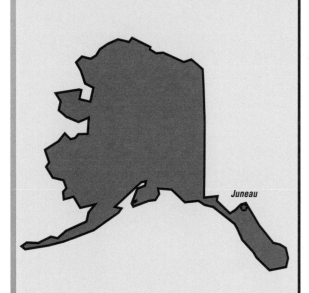

Juneau

WORD SEARCH

```
A C P R O S P E C T C R E E K M P B E W
L B R O U L C U J T R R I U G W D C Z O
D S E Q D V F X G R C W B M J A S M A P
B O Y G Z E O A Y B I T S D N I P K W E
Y A S H U T N U M L A L T F G S I V G N
P R O S F V Q A G H W O I L B H P Y O K
M C L O W R I B L X I M E J P J E Y L M
E M O N S A I G O I F B N L C N L K D R
E S K P H O W U G N Y P A I Y J I R W N
G F U A L B Y D A J L Y H F K L N D S A
P A L I W P L N P G V D W D S B E O Z J
N M B V C I S F R C O Q R U A T V A E K
D S I J F O L L Y I Z A T D R D V T L B
R H Y D J N G L Y H W E S O B Z L B R T
K D N U R I C G X E J C O R P A N N M H
F E U M E F S Z S W B K F A J V C E V Y
I L O F D R E S I V D R E T H B T D W L
G P K R M H A M C U T G L I E O Y W T X
H S F P T K G K J V B O V D S Q V N E K
J U N E A U Q P G M U T Q I D W H X F S
```

WORDS
Denali
Folly
Gold
Iditarod
Juneau
Nome
Oil
Pipeline
Prospect Creek
Seward

How Alaska Got Its Name

The name comes from the Aleut word *alaxsxaq,* meaning "great land," or "the object toward which the action of the sea is directed." Alaska is also called the Land of the Midnight Sun, and America's Last Frontier.

Historic Sites

✪ Sitka National Historical Park, featuring authentic totem poles (!)

State Trivia

✪ The Trans-Alaska Pipeline carries oil across 800 miles, making it available to all the eager customers!

✪ Juneau is the only United States capital city that can only be reached by boat or plane. It also covers more ground than any other city in the country— over 3,000 square miles.

✪ In 1927, thirteen-year-old Benny Benson entered his flag design in a contest to decide the territorial flag. His winning entry later became the official state flag that still flies today.

✪ Did you know that Nome was actually named by accident? Someone making a map of the area wrote down "name?" but the person copying the map thought it said "Nome." There's an argument for having neater handwriting!

✪ Every winter, Alaska holds the 1,049-mile dogsled race called the Iditarod. Is Fido up for it?

✪ You know how some days feel so much longer than others? Well, when residents of Barrow complain about that, they're not imagining things! After the sun rises here on May 10, it doesn't set again for almost three months. Barrow also has the shortest day—when the sun sets on November 18, it isn't seen again for nearly three months.

CROSSWORD

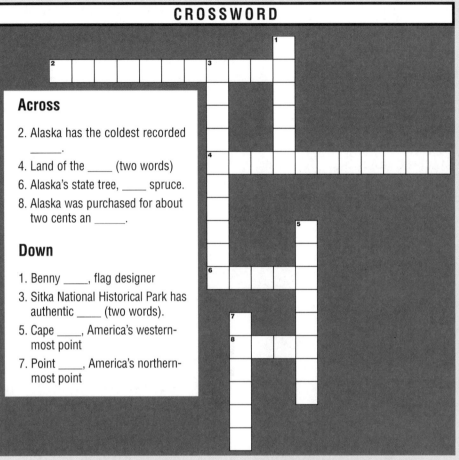

Across

2. Alaska has the coldest recorded _____.
4. Land of the _____ (two words)
6. Alaska's state tree, _____ spruce.
8. Alaska was purchased for about two cents an _____.

Down

1. Benny _____, flag designer
3. Sitka National Historical Park has authentic _____ (two words).
5. Cape _____, America's western-most point
7. Point _____, America's northern-most point

Arizona

DATE OF STATEHOOD:
February 14, 1912

STATE CAPITAL: Phoenix

STATE TREE: Paloverde
(green-barked acacia)

STATE FLOWER: Saguaro flower

STATE BIRD: Cactus wren

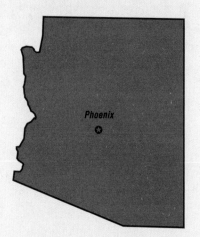

Phoenix

Arizona may have been the last of the forty-eight contiguous (touching) states to be admitted to the union, but it's certainly not the least important! The state is home to several big tourist attractions, including one of the seven natural wonders of the world—the Grand Canyon. The canyon, two billion years old, is a total of 277 miles long. Visitors who travel to the bottom have to remember to bring water, because the canyon is one mile deep— so deep that the climate changes as you travel down, becoming significantly hotter. Near Flagstaff is another extraordinary sight, a giant crater—600 feet deep and a mile wide—left by a meteor crash millions of years ago. And located in Flagstaff itself is the Lowell Observatory, where astronomers discovered the planet Pluto in 1930!

How Arizona Got Its Name

The name comes from the Papago Indian term *aleh-zon,* meaning "little spring," which originally referred to a small spring in the territory that is now part of Mexico. Arizona is also known as the Grand Canyon State.

Historic Sites

✪ Grand Canyon

✪ Navajo National Monument

State Trivia

✪ If you hate having to change your clock twice a year for Daylight Savings Time, maybe you should move to Arizona. Residents there are on Mountain Standard time all year long, *except* at the Navajo Nation.

✪ The famous "Gunfight at O.K. Corral" took place at Tombstone on October 26, 1881.

✪ The London Bridge was transported all the way from England to Lake Havasu City, where it's carefully preserved. No more danger of it "falling down!" There's also a bridge on the Salt River built just for sheep— it was measured to be "one sheep" wide.

✪ Yuma has the special distinction of being the sunniest city in America—it's sunny 90 percent of the time here!

✪ The famous Native American leader Geronimo led the Apache resistance in Arizona for many years. He was such a successful fighter that rumors circulated about his supernatural powers. If he had any, they ran out on September 4, 1886, when he was finally captured.

✪ Watch what you wear around your neck when you're in town— the bola tie is the official state neckwear!

Arkansas

DATE OF STATEHOOD:
June 15, 1836

STATE CAPITAL: Little Rock

STATE TREE: Pine

STATE FLOWER: Apple blossom

STATE BIRD: Mockingbird

Little Rock

Arkansas is clearly determined to make itself stand out! Surrounded by mostly flatland states, its Boston Mountains—part of the Ozarks—stretch up into the sky. It's also the only state to pass a resolution on how to pronounce its name. State legislature made an official decree in 1881 that the last "s" is silent. And in 1957, during the heated racial tensions in the South, nine African-American students braved the protests and threats to enroll in an all-white high school in Little Rock, their courage setting them apart and paving the way for the school—along with others in the South—to become safely integrated.

How Arkansas Got Its Name

The name is derived from the French pronunciation of "Kansas," the Algonquian name for the Quapaw tribe encountered here by the French explorers Jacques Marquette and Louis Jolliet. Arkansas is also called the Land of Opportunity, the Razorback State, and the Natural State.

President Born Here!

✪ William Jefferson Clinton, 42nd president

Historic Sites

✪ Old Washington Historic State Park, Hope

✪ Pioneer Village, Rison

✪ Arkansas Territorial Restoration, Little Rock

✪ Mountain Village 1890, Bull Shoals

✪ Ozark Folk Center State Park, Mountain View

✪ Robinson Farm Museum and Heritage Centers, Valley Springs

State Trivia

✪ Stop by the Crater of Diamonds State Park, where visitors can mine for real diamonds. You might get lucky—the largest diamond found here was over forty carats!

✪ The 1811 earthquake in Arkansas has been called the strongest one to hit the continent.

✪ Some people believe that the Hot Springs—with water that heats up as high as 147 degrees Fahrenheit *naturally*—have healing powers. Babe Ruth and Franklin D. Roosevelt must have thought so—they're two of the many visitors who have taken a dip here over the years!

California

DATE OF STATEHOOD:
September 9, 1850

STATE CAPITAL: Sacramento

STATE TREE: California
redwood

STATE FLOWER: Golden poppy

STATE BIRD: California valley
quail

Where can you find both the highest and lowest points in the Continental United States? Not only does California have two completely different climates in its northern and southern areas, but it reaches 14,494 feet above sea level at Mt. Whitney, and dips 282 feet *below* sea level as in Death Valley. It's also the most populous state in the Union, with over 31 million residents. But a 3,500-year-old tree nicknamed "General Sherman," and a 4,000-year-old stand of bristlecone pines (no nickname!) have been here much longer than all those people—they're among the world's oldest living things. And though visitors to cool Northern California might have trouble believing it, the state also holds the record for the hottest temperature—134 degrees Fahrenheit in Death Valley on July 10, 1913.

Sacramento

CALIFORNIA REPUBLIC

WORD SEARCH

```
A N B Q J G O N C E S P H O V B R I S R
J S I S L A N D U N V B T L G Y F R Y C
G H R Q O D W E Y L F W E E L C P K U T
S Z U E N J X E S H O N U B K B I P W F
H M B T W S I L I C O N V A L L E Y D T
E S A S H V R S Y C Z C T W P E Y A Y J
R L I G V M L O E B K J N D R F G H U N
M O Q R H B M L T V A F P G L A J C L H
A G E C O X T C K I E O L D E S T R M A
N J L W J S I A Z G N L P W J L T B Y I
E T K A I K P M O C B E A L D U F D E L
I C R R T O U N F W T V K A H S D I T A
A S B L N D G S D J P A U W Q K L K L B
D U T R O G O L D E N R D L F X O V N R
M R E Z F Z G E D M L X E S E V G T G E
J H E J X E B N P W M B K R O G M H R A
S G U D P O S S Q C V H U C V K N T L D
P L A N D W H M Y N C I S N I Y R A M K
R E T V P R C O M P U T E R B H Y N R Y
F P I M S C O I U S V D M N Y F E I E O
```

WORDS	Gold	La Brea	Sherman
Bristlecone	Golden	Oldest	Silicon Valley
Computer	Island	Orange	

How California Got Its Name

Spanish explorers Hernán Cortés and Fortún Ximenez took the name of a fictional island in writer García Ordóñez's *Las Sergas de Esplandián,* "California," and gave it to the Baja California Peninsula. California's most popular nicknames are the Golden State and the Empire State of the West.

President Born Here!

❂ Richard Nixon, 37th president

Historic Sites

❂ Yosemite National Park

❂ La Brea Tar Pits, Los Angeles—where bones of Ice Age animals are stuck in oil.

State Trivia

❂ Not only does she have a Dream House and a hot convertible, but Barbie also has her very own Hall of Fame in Palo Alto! Started by a private collector, the building holds around 20,000 Barbie figures and related items, going all the way back to 1959.

❂ Wacky but true: It used to be against the law in California to peel an orange in a hotel room. (What if you just cut it into slices instead?)

❂ Los Angeles's first movie theater opened on April 2, 1902. Since then, the little town of Hollywood has become the film capital of the country.

❂ In 1849, the famous "forty-niners" rushed across the country to California for its newly discovered gold. Within a year, over $30 million in gold had been found.

❂ Today, it's technology that drives the market. Silicon Valley in San Jose is renowned for its numerous computer companies—companies that are constantly producing new and innovative computer products to keep the industry growing.

❂ Located in the middle of the San Francisco Bay, Alcatraz Island is still home to the famous Alcatraz Prison—though the jail itself is no longer in use. Once known for being nearly impossible to escape, the prison is now one of the Golden Gate National Recreation Area's most popular destinations. First everyone wanted out, and now they want in. Go figure!

CROSSWORD

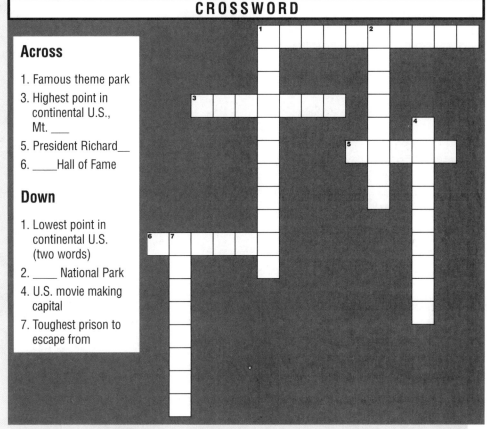

Across

1. Famous theme park
3. Highest point in continental U.S., Mt. ___
5. President Richard__
6. ____Hall of Fame

Down

1. Lowest point in continental U.S. (two words)
2. ____ National Park
4. U.S. movie making capital
7. Toughest prison to escape from

Colorado

DATE OF STATEHOOD:
August 1,1876

STATE CAPITAL: Denver

STATE TREE: Colorado blue spruce

STATE FLOWER: Rocky Mountain columbine (AKA white and lavender columbine)

STATE BIRD: Lark bunting

The song "America the Beautiful," celebrating our country's natural riches, was written by Katherine Lee Bates in 1893 after she traveled up Pikes Peak. The breathtaking view that inspired her continues to overwhelm anyone who visits this stunning state. The tallest sand dunes in North America can be found at the Great Sand Dunes National Monument—reaching around 700 feet high. And although one third of Colorado is actually prairie land, the rest of the state has fifty-four mountains over 14,000 feet high—more than any other state in the country! Colorado also has the nation's largest cliff dwelling, Mesa Verde, where an Anasazi Native American tribe built a four-storied city centuries ago.

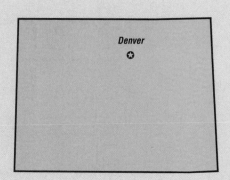

Denver

MAZE

How Colorado Got Its Name

Colorado, the Spanish word for "red," was chosen because of the red waters of the Colorado River. The state is also called the Centennial State, the Highest State, and the Switzerland of America.

Historic Site

✪ Mesa Verde cliff dwelling

State Trivia

✪ American athletes gearing up for the Olympics train at the U.S. Olympic Center in Colorado Springs. However, Colorado is the only state in history to decline hosting the Olympics event itself! Denver had the chance in 1976, but residents didn't want the hassle.

✪ The United States Air Force Academy, the Figure Skating Hall of Fame, and the Pro Rodeo Hall of Champions are also located in Colorado Springs. (Strange combination there, don't you think?)

✪ The world's first rodeo was held in Deer Trail on July 4th, 1869. Yee-haw!

✪ No wonder one of Colorado's nicknames is the Highest State. Denver is also the highest state capital, at one mile above sea level.

✪ Louis Ballast of Denver trademarked the cheeseburger in 1935 when he served it at his Humpty-Dumpty drive-in restaurant, leading to the city's claim to have invented the tasty sandwich.

✪ Drivers on Highway 103 travel along the highest paved road in North America. If they ride to the top of Mount Evans, they've made a whopping 14,264-foot-high road trip!

✪ Famous native! The *Titanic* passenger Molly Brown, dubbed Unsinkable Molly Brown after her valiant efforts to save fellow passengers from the sinking ship, was born in Colorado.

✪ Fountain was chosen as the country's millennium city, because its population best represents the makeup of America's "melting pot" of people.

CROSSWORD

Across

2. Great Sand _____ National Monument
5. Pro _____ Hall of Champions
7. Nation's largest cliff dwelling (two words)
8. Rocky _____

Down

1. Louis Ballast's delicious creation
3. Millenium city
4. Famous world sporting event
6. "Unsinkable Molly _____"

Connecticut

DATE OF STATEHOOD:
January 9, 1788

STATE CAPITAL: Hartford

STATE TREE: White oak

STATE FLOWER: Mountain laurel

STATE BIRD: American robin

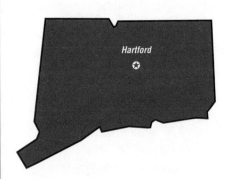

Connecticut is a state of impressive "firsts." The first pay phone showed up in Hartford in 1889, and the first public art museum—Wadsworth Atheneum—opened its doors in 1842. The first atomic-powered submarine, *U.S.S. Nautilus,* was launched from its base in Groton in 1954. The written word is obviously pretty important here too. Noah Webster, a Connecticut native, published the first American dictionary in 1806, just a few years after the first American cookbook (*American Cookery,* by Amelia Simmons) was published in Hartford. And the state is *also* home to the country's first newspaper, the *Connecticut Courant* (now called the *Hartford Courant*). Whew!

How Connecticut Got Its Name

The name comes from *quinneh-tukqut,* meaning "beside the long tidal river." Connecticut's official nickname is the Constitution State, but it's also known as the Nutmeg State and the Land of Steady Habits.

State Trivia

⊗ The Barnum Museum in Bridgeport honors hometown hero P. T. Barnum, of Barnum and Bailey Circus.

⊗ Ever seen the movie *Mystic Pizza?* The *real* Mystic Pizza restaurant can be found in the small seaport town of Mystic—but don't expect it to look the way it does in the movie!

⊗ "Let's get ready to rumble!" Wrestling fans might like to know that the WWF headquarters are located in Stamford.

⊗ More firsts! Connecticut also had the first: Law school (at Litchfield in 1784), insurance company (1795), and use of anesthesia, by Dr. Horace Wells in Hartford in 1844.

⊗ Have you heard of the Connecticut tea party? Probably not, but in 1770 Old Lyme residents got the jump on Boston when they seized and burned tea from peddlers to protest the high British taxes.

Delaware

DATE OF STATEHOOD:
December 7, 1787

STATE CAPITAL: Dover

STATE TREE: American holly
(AKA white holly)

STATE FLOWER: Peach blossom

STATE BIRD: Blue hen chicken

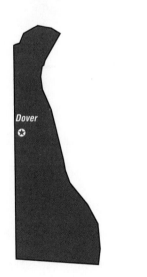

The first state to ratify the Constitution, Delaware earned its nickname as the Diamond State when President Thomas Jefferson compared the state to the beautiful gem. His reason? The state was like a diamond in that it was "small but of great value." And Delaware has lived up to these words, becoming a leader in American industry. Nylon, an important synthetic fiber, was invented in a factory here. The DuPont Company headquarters in Wilmington have contributed to the city being called the chemical capital of the world. And the Delaware River is used to ship goods all along the East Coast, keeping businesses everywhere running smoothly.

How Delaware Got Its Name

The state was named after Sir Thomas West, Lord De La Warr, the first governor of Virginia. Nicknames for Delaware include the First State, the Diamond State, and the Peach State.

State Trivia

✪ Delaware isn't *all* about business! The Cypress Swamp has the country's northernmost natural group of cypress trees.

✪ The first log cabins in North America were built in Delaware in 1683 by Swedish immigrants, and one of the cabins has actually been preserved over all these years! It's on display at the Delaware Agricultural Museum in Dover.

✪ The first steam railroad train chugged out of New Castle in 1831.

✪ One of Delaware's products—Fisher's caramel popcorn, served along the state's coast—is so popular it's ordered from places as far away as Vietnam and Indonesia!

✪ Heard of the Heimlich maneuver? Dr. Henry Heimlich, a Delaware native, invented the quick and easy procedure to help stop a person from choking to death.

✪ Because Delaware was the first state to ratify the Constitution, it enjoys the honor of leading the parade of states every four years at the Presidential Inauguration!

Florida

DATE OF STATEHOOD:
March 3, 1845

STATE CAPITAL: Tallahassee

STATE TREE: Sabal palmetto palm

STATE FLOWER: Orange blossom

STATE BIRD: Mockingbird

It's not hard to figure out why Florida's such a hot tourist spot! After Alaska, it has the second longest coastline in the United States, with 4,000 miles of beautiful beaches. Nicknamed the Sunshine State because it's sunny and warm year-round, Florida is also packed with things to do and see. Orlando alone draws more than 30 million visitors each year to its theme parks, including Disney World, Sea World, Universal Studios, and Epcot Center. If that's not enough, then Tampa also has Busch Gardens! But there's more to the state than its famous theme parks. The Everglades, one of the world's largest swamps, has alligators, crocodiles, panthers, bobcats, and sea turtles. The John F. Kennedy Space Center at Cape Canaveral is responsible for several significant moments in space exploration: in 1961, Alan Shepard became the first American in space; the following year, John Glenn orbited Earth. And in 1969, Neil Armstrong got the chance to stroll on the moon!

Tallahassee

WORD SCRAMBLE

neyisd _____

redsavegle _____

asnilpneu _____

seyk _____

heusnisn _____

mgrartsno _____

lcvanaaer _____

tedaroag _____

How Florida Got Its Name

Explorer Ponce de León arrived here on Easter Sunday, leading him to name the area *La Florida* to commemorate the Spanish Easter holiday, Pascua Florida ("flowering Easter"). Florida is also known as the Sunshine State, the Alligator State, the Everglades State, the Orange State, and the Southernmost State.

State Trivia

✪ St. Augustine, the oldest city in the United States, was founded by the Spanish explorer Don Pedro Menendez de Avilesin in 1565.

✪ Chances are that the last orange or grapefruit you ate was from Florida, since three quarters of the nation's supply of these fruits are grown in the state.

✪ The International Swimming Hall of Fame is located in Ft. Lauderdale, and Palm Beach Gardens is home to the Professional Golf Association Hall of Fame.

✪ The first bank Automated Teller Machine (ATM) was installed in Miami especially for inline skaters. There's some special treatment!

✪ Gatorade, the popular sports drink, was originally developed by a University of Florida Gators coach for his team. That's how it got its unusual name!

✪ Ever wonder where the Guinness Record–breaking strawberry shortcake was made? Wonder no more! The 827-square-foot, 6,000-pound cake was created in McCall Park in Plant City.

CROSSWORD

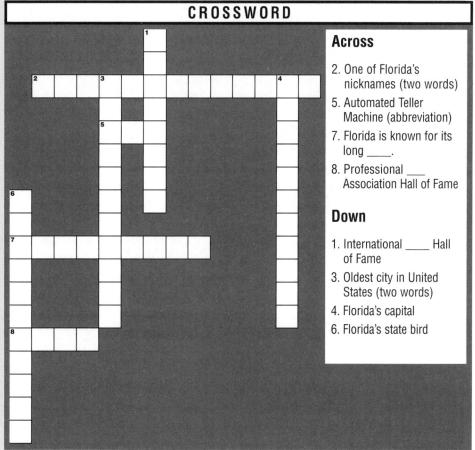

Across

2. One of Florida's nicknames (two words)
5. Automated Teller Machine (abbreviation)
7. Florida is known for its long ____.
8. Professional ___ Association Hall of Fame

Down

1. International ____ Hall of Fame
3. Oldest city in United States (two words)
4. Florida's capital
6. Florida's state bird

Georgia

DATE OF STATEHOOD:
January 2, 1788

STATE CAPITAL: Atlanta

STATE TREE: Live oak

STATE FLOWER: Cherokee rose

STATE BIRD: Brown thrasher

Georgia has both a rich history and a significant role in today's changing culture. Born in Atlanta on January 15, 1929, Martin Luther King, Jr., first preached at the Ebenezer Baptist Church in his native city before going on to become a national leader of African-Americans. Wesleyan College in Macon was the first college in the world to grant degrees to women. (Yeah, Wesleyan!) And today, Atlanta stays involved in the country's industry as the home of Coca-Cola headquarters along with Ted Turner's media empire, which includes popular cable networks such as CNN.

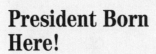

Atlanta

How Georgia Got Its Name

James Oglethorpe named the state after King George II of England. Georgia has many nicknames, including the Empire State of the South, the Peach State, the Goober State, the Buzzard State, and the Yankee-Land of the South.

President Born Here!

Jimmy Carter, 39th president

State Trivia

- Anyone in the mood for a Thin Mint? Girl Scout founder Juliette Low grew up in Savannah, Georgia's oldest city. Her home can now be visited by tourists, along with other houses nearby that have been preserved from the 1700s.

- Baseball great Jackie Robinson was born in Cairo, and author Alice Walker is an Eatontown native.

- Okefenokee Swamp, the world's largest freshwater swamp, has over 700 square miles filled with fifty-four species of reptiles, forty-nine types of mammals, and 234 kinds of birds. Sheesh—how do they keep them straight?

- Chickamauga and Chattanooga National Military Park is the site of the bloodiest battle in American history, the Battle of Chickamauga.

- Georgia is known for its peaches, but it's also the leading producer of peanuts and pecans, and the only state that grows the world-famous sweet Vidalia onion.

Hawaii

DATE OF STATEHOOD:
August 21, 1959

STATE CAPITAL: Honolulu

STATE TREE: Kukui (candlenut)

STATE FLOWER: Yellow hibiscus

STATE BIRD: Nene (Hawaiian goose)

The name *Hawaii* actually refers to both the entire state and to one of the islands that makes up the state. There are 132 islands in total, but only the eight largest are inhabited. Originally formed by undersea volcanoes, the islands of Hawaii still have active volcanoes today. (Scary!) In fact, Kilauea, on the island of Hawaii, is the world's most active volcano, and Mauna Loa, another active volcano on Hawaii, is the world's largest mountain mass. Despite the presence of these natural dangers—and the fact that Mt. Waialeale is the wettest place on Earth— the overall climate in Hawaii is so pleasant that the Hawaiian language has no word for "weather," because it's always so nice!

Honolulu

How Hawaii Got Its Name

There are several theories about how this state was named. One legend is that the man who discovered the islands was named Hawaii Loa. It's also thought that the name could come from the word *hawa,* meaning "homeland," and the suffix *ii,* meaning "small." The official nickname is the Aloha State. Hawaii is also called the Pineapple State, the Paradise of the Pacific, and the Youngest State.

State Trivia

✪ Surfing was invented in Hawaii years ago by—believe it or not—kings and chieftains. Can you picture those guys catching the waves before holding court with their subjects?

✪ English and Hawaiian are both official languages here. The Hawaiian language only has twelve letters—a, e, i, o, u, h, k, l, m, n, p, w. It must get confusing, because the Hawaiian word *aloha* has several different meanings: welcome, goodbye, love, and friendship.

✪ Residents of Hawaii enjoy their very own time zone, Hawaiian Standard Time.

✪ Feel like pretending to be a prince or a princess for a day? Then visit Iolani Palace, the only royal palace in the United States.

✪ Hawaii is the only state that grows coffee beans. It's also known for its pineapple and sugar production.

✪ Each inhabited island of Hawaii has its own color: Hawaii, red; Maui, pink; Molokai, green; Kahoolawe, gray; Lanai, yellow; Oahu, yellow (again!); Kauai, purple; Niihau, white.

Idaho

DATE OF STATEHOOD:
July 3, 1890

STATE CAPITAL: Boise

STATE TREE: Western white pine

STATE FLOWER: Idaho syringa

STATE BIRD: Mountain bluebird

Boise

When most people think of Idaho, they imagine potatoes—and lots of 'em! In fact, a full quarter of the United States crop of potatoes do come from Idaho, where about 27 billion spuds are grown every year. That's a lot of french fries! But Idaho has more to it than just its well known starchy vegetable. Visitors to the state can check out the deepest gorge in America, Hells Canyon. They can also walk along the Craters of the Moon, brightly colored lava fields and craters from extinct volcanoes that look so much like the surface of the moon, NASA astronauts once trained there! But anyone who's still interested in potatoes can travel to Shelley, where the Idaho Annual Spud Day has been celebrated every year since 1927.

How Idaho Got Its Name

If you can't think of a good name, then just make one up, right? That must have been what George M. Willing was thinking when he invented the name "Idaho," an artificial Indian word. But at least Idaho's nicknames are for real— the state is known as the Gem State, the Gem of the Mountains, and the Potato State.

State Trivia

⚙ The National Oldtime Fiddler's Contest is held annually in Weiser. (Do you think they get up on the roof to play?)

⚙ Sun Valley is the site of America's first ski resort, founded in 1935.

⚙ What a drag! The entire town of American Falls had to be moved in the mid-1920s when the original American Falls Dam was constructed.

⚙ Soda Springs has the world's largest man-made geyser.

⚙ Need some exercise? Try a jaunt down America's longest main street in Island Park—it's 33 miles long!

WORD SEARCH

```
A C F I O B K B J A G N I R Y S B N F F
I H T W Q Y V R E S N W T B T I G O I I
N S M E G E M T E A B I G P W P L P D T
B J L Y H V J W R R I P T A R C V E D M
R Y Q A U M X S P Z E L J O N W C R L C
F E V N N E S F M I Y S P U D S G L E P
M A L K Y D S K N U O K T B N E T Y R N
G C W A L S P G P A T C W G Y I B A N E
A R H M Q L Q A C U O K Z Y H F S S X A
B O I S E R G Y R S F H E J U K U U I V
P W S O T O E P U K I G O R C R N L N W
B M G W A Z Y M B V H S L H P H V F K U
I G O V I C U E K W B V S R A M A E O J
P C Y U S I S E A T Q R J L N V L N M E
O J E X H V F R Y H E S F T C W L I T A
A Q L W L B S C L T C M B N H R E S Y P
N R L J T L N J A S K I E L S J Y R T G
L S E T C I U R S B Y V C T O B W U L V
E R H K N S C U S N U H P J R E T S M F
B G S P E M G L R A O E N I G E Y S E R
```

WORDS

Boise · Craters · Fiddler · Gem · Geyser · Island Park · Shelley · Spuds · Sun Valley · Syringa

☼ The perfect spot for your very first rafting trip! Malad River is the shortest river in the world.

☼ North America's tallest single structured sand dune can be found at Bruneau Dunes State Park. It's 470 feet high.

☼ Idaho even has a "Niagara of the West"—Shoshone Falls. The water spills over a 212-foot drop.

☼ We told you there was more than just potatoes—Rigby is actually known as the birthplace of TV! That's because it's the hometown of Philo T. Farnsworth, a pioneer of television technology.

CROSSWORD

Across

1. NASA _____ trained at Craters of the Moon
5. _____ Falls
6. Town that had to be moved (two words)
8. Deepest gorge in America (two words)

Down

2. Why Rigby is famous
3. Location of world's largest man-made geyser (two words)
4. Idaho's best known crop
7. Shortest river in the world

☼ Heaven's Gate Lookout, atop Seven Devils Peaks, offers a true scenic over-look—from here, you can see into four states!

☼ Idaho's state seal, which became official in 1891, is the only state seal designed by a woman.

Illinois

DATE OF STATEHOOD:
December 3, 1818

STATE CAPITAL: Springfield

STATE TREE: White oak

STATE FLOWER: Violet

STATE BIRD: Cardinal

Springfield may be the capital of Illinois, but Chicago is definitely the state's most famous city. The Chicago Cubs play at Wrigley Field, one of the oldest and best-loved baseball parks in the country. O'Hare Airport, located in the Windy City, is the world's busiest airport. And above all, Chicago is known for its amazing architecture. It has the tallest building in the United States—the Sears Tower—which stands 1,454 feet tall and 110 stories high. Its Monadnock Building is the tallest building made entirely of masonry. And the ten-story Home Insurance Building, constructed in 1885, was the first skyscraper. Chicago residents really *do* have their heads in the clouds—they have to in order to see everything!

Springfield

ILLINOIS

WORD SEARCH

```
D A C N V E X I R K T W H I T E O A K B
L I R U I V Y U W S E T G M T P G C F G
C O N Y U S A L I S Y C W L D S O K S A
D Q S O X I N W N C M J D T N N T P R R
N W B F S F Z S D G L H B K D J O B O C
A J E Y Y A C N Y U D Y N A M C R E G H
O T I E V G U L I J O P N J L O E N Q I
F Y R Z O A R R M E H O P A X K F R T T
U A I I P W E S S N M O M E B D K T A E
I R A J M O N J D P R W L C Q R C M W C
G W R G L I N B A R B E T N I D P E H T
P M P T W V Y S H I E W H G J L B G O U
V B P D D I H F T M T P U K F O M N D R
H Q L N A C B P X B I F A V O J D L S E
C T S P R I N G F I E L D R R V A J E I
R K Z C U K Z A E K U K Y U C H G H S L
A X U H B T R K F V N C M I Z S P L C F
D S I L O P O R T E M R R W S M Y F I J
S H A K R V Y E Y W V W U H P Y V K J H
A M E N D M E N T F N S P R G I N D S D
```

WORDS	Dinosaurs	Prairie	White Oak
Amendment	Metropolis	Skyscraper	Windy
Architecture	Monadnock	Springfield	

How Illinois Got Its Name

The name comes from an Illinois and Peoria Indian word, *ilini,* which means "man" or "warrior." The state's official nickname is the Land of Lincoln, but it's also called the Prairie State and the Corn State.

President Born Here!

✪ Ronald Reagan, 40th president

State Trivia

✪ Looking for Superman? Maybe you'll find the man of steel himself in the real-life town of Metropolis, located in the southern part of the state.

✪ Chicago may have had the first skyscraper, but it was Des Plaines where the first "golden arches" went up. The McDonald's chain opened its original fast food franchise restaurant here in 1955.

✪ Illinois was the first state to ratify the 13th amendment abolishing slavery, in 1865. (Good job, Illinois!)

✪ George Ferris built (what else?) the world's first Ferris wheel in Chicago in 1893.

✪ Maybe all those tall buildings reminded him of dinosaurs— *Jurassic Park* author Michael Crichton is an Illinois native.

✪ Abraham Lincoln lived here from the age of 21 until the time he became president, serving in the state legislature and practicing law in Springfield. Fellow president Ulysses S. Grant also lived here for many years.

✪ The first aquarium opened in Chicago in 1893. As if the city didn't have enough going on!

✪ Even though known gangster John Dillinger was shot by the FBI at Chicago's Biograph Theater, moviegoers still catch the newest flicks at the theater!

CROSSWORD

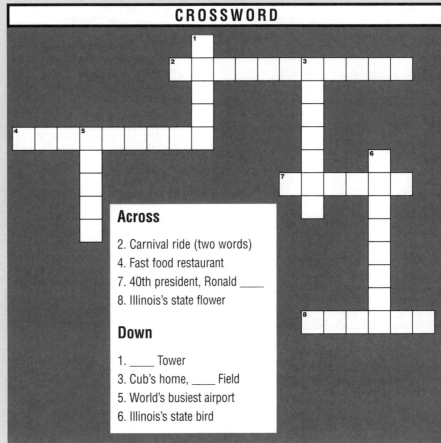

Across

2. Carnival ride (two words)
4. Fast food restaurant
7. 40th president, Ronald ____
8. Illinois's state flower

Down

1. ____ Tower
3. Cub's home, ____ Field
5. World's busiest airport
6. Illinois's state bird

Indiana

DATE OF STATEHOOD:
December 11, 1816

STATE CAPITAL: Indianapolis

STATE TREE: Tulip tree
(AKA Tulip poplar)

STATE FLOWER: Peony

STATE BIRD: Cardinal

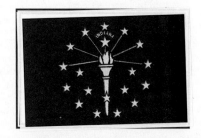

Indiana is certainly a sports-loving state! It's home to the Indianapolis 500, the annual Memorial Day auto race that draws people from across the country. During the rest of the year, fans can visit the Auto Racing Hall of Fame, also in Indianapolis. For drivers who aren't up to racing cars, the town of Twelve Mile holds the Annual 500 Riding Lawn Mowers Race, where opponents race—no joke—lawn mowers. Football, basketball, and baseball are also revered in Indiana. The College Football Hall of Fame is located in South Bend, Indiana, and the first major league baseball game was played at Fort Wayne in 1871. The home-state is also very proud of its hero, Larry Bird, a champion basketball player who returned after retiring as a player to coach the Indiana Pacers.

MAZE

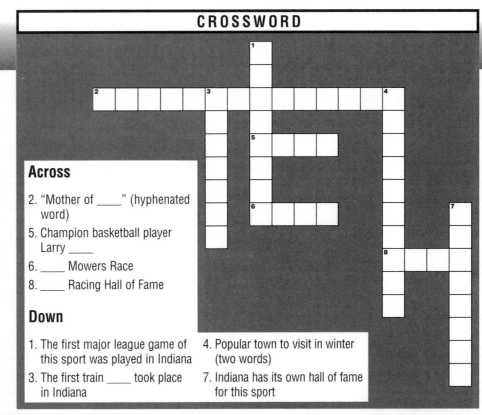

CROSSWORD

Across

2. "Mother of ____" (hyphenated word)
5. Champion basketball player Larry ____
6. ____ Mowers Race
8. ____ Racing Hall of Fame

Down

1. The first major league game of this sport was played in Indiana
3. The first train ____ took place in Indiana
4. Popular town to visit in winter (two words)
7. Indiana has its own hall of fame for this sport

How Indiana Got Its Name

When Congress established the territory in 1800, they gave it the name "Indiana," meaning "Land of the Indians." The state is also called the Hoosier State, and the Mother of Vice Presidents.

State Trivia

✪ Surprise—more sports stuff! The state has its very own Indiana Football Hall of Fame, in Richmond. The International Palace of Sports Hall of Fame is located in Warsaw, and the United States Track and Field Hall of Fame can be found in Angola.

✪ Who knew you needed a farm for goldfish? Apparently someone thought so, because the first one was opened in Martinsville in 1899.

✪ Indiana earned the nickname as the Mother of Vice Presidents after five of its natives made it to the second highest office in the country: Schuyler Colfax, Thomas A. Hendricks, Charles W. Fairbanks, Thomas Marshall, and Dan Quayle.

✪ The lucky students at Indiana University get to lounge around in the largest student union building in the world. The Indiana University Memorial Union building has over 475,000 square feet of space!

✪ It's a questionable honor, sure, but Indiana was the site of the country's first train robbery, in 1866. The Reno brothers made off with $15,000.

✪ Though known for all of its sports mania, Indiana is also a top producer of musical instruments.

✪ Did you ever send a letter to Santa Claus? If so, it might have ended up in a little town in Indiana called—you guessed it—Santa Claus. According to residents, people flock here in winter simply to send letters with the town's name on the postmark!

✪ Times sure have changed! When the very first long-distance auto race was held at the Indianapolis Speedway on May 30, 1911, the winner drove an average speed of 75 miles per hour and took home 14,000 dollars. Today, drivers in the Indy 500 race average 167 miles per hour and compete for a prize of over 1.2 million dollars!

✪ The famous (and much loved) Raggedy Ann doll was created by Indianapolis resident Marcella Gruelle in 1914.

✪ Airplane inventor Wilbur Wright was born in Millville in 1867.

25

Iowa

DATE OF STATEHOOD:
December 28, 1846

STATE CAPITAL: Des Moines

STATE TREE: Oak

STATE FLOWER: Wild rose

STATE BIRD: Eastern goldfinch

One of America's leading farm states, Iowa is unique in that roughly 97 percent of its land is cultivated. With the state's focus on farming, it's impressive that the literacy rate in Iowa is actually higher than anywhere else in the country. Maybe the hard work on the fields inspire reading, or maybe it's the yummy snacks—Iowa has the nation's largest popcorn processing plant *and* the biggest cereal-making plant (Quaker Oats, in Cedar Rapids).

Des Moines

IOWA

How Iowa Got Its Name

The name comes from the Iowa Indian word *ayuxwa,* meaning "beautiful land." The word was misspelled by both the French and the British as "Ayoua," and "Ioway" (oops!). Iowa's been nicknamed the Hawkeye State, the Land Where the Tall Corn Grows, the Nation's Breadbasket, and the Corn State.

President Born Here!

Herbert Hoover, 31st President

Historic Sites

✪ Living History Farms, near Des Moines

✪ Heritage Village, Des Moines

✪ Bentonsport-National Historic District, Fairfield

✪ Kalona Historical Village, Kalona

✪ Pella Historical Village Museum, Pella

State Trivia

✪ The National Balloon Museum in Indianola has over 200 years of "ballooning history." (How much can there really be, right?)

✪ Famous Iowa natives include actor John Wayne, born in Winterset in 1907, and William "Buffalo Bill" Cody, born in Le Clair in 1846.

✪ During the Civil War, the legal cutoff age for soldiers was 45. But Iowa had a special "Greybeard Regiment" made up of men over this age who were still determined to fight.

✪ An old water tower in Stanton was renovated by residents to be the world's largest coffee pot. (They *definitely* had too much time on their hands!)

✪ Mmm . . . delicious. Iowa developed the apple that lives up to its official brand name: Delicious.

Kansas

DATE OF SATEHOOD:
January 29, 1861

STATE CAPITAL: Topeka

STATE TREE: Cottonwood

STATE FLOWER: Wild sunflower

STATE BIRD: Western meadowlark

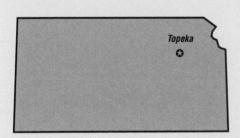

It's hard to believe that a state known for its cowboy history would also be famous for groundbreaking events, but Kansas has done it all! Dodge City was once full of cowboys and buffalo hunters who were kept in line by legendary sheriffs, including the renowned Wyatt Earp. But Kansas also became the first state to elect a woman mayor when Susanna Salter took office in Argonia in 1887. And in 1954, Kansas again took a major step forward when the Brown vs. Board of Education Supreme Court trial—originating in Topeka on behalf of young Linda Brown—declared school segregation unconstitutional.

How Kansas Got Its Name

The name comes from the Kansas Indian word *kanze,* meaning "south wind." During the conflict between free and slave states before the Civil War, Kansas was called the Bleeding State. Since then, its other nicknames include the Sunflower State, the Cyclone State, the Squatter State, and the Jayhawk State.

State Trivia

✪ Kansans were the first lucky people to taste Pizza Hut pizza when the original restaurant opened.

✪ Amelia Earhart, the aviation pioneer who made the first solo flight from Hawaii to California, was born in Atchison.

✪ Talk about a weird idea for a zoo! In Abilene there's a Microzoo full of micro-organisms that aren't even visible to the naked eye.

✪ Helium was discovered by University of Kansas scientists in 1905. How long do you it think took for them to get tired of listening to each other talk in funny voices?

✪ The first shopping center opened in Kansas City in 1922. What an exciting day that must have been for bargain hunters!

✪ Kansas City is also home to the Agricultural Hall of Fame—not surprising since the state is a major producer of wheat, corn, and soybeans. But there's another that is a little strange—The Greyhound Racing Hall of Fame is located in Abilene.

Kentucky

DATE OF STATEHOOD:
June 1, 1792

STATE CAPITAL: Frankfort

STATE TREE: Coffee tree

STATE FLOWER: Goldenrod

STATE BIRD: Cardinal

Every year, on the first Saturday in May, spectators swarm to Churchill Downs in Louisville for the biggest horse event of the year: The Kentucky Derby. Along with hosting this all-important race, Kentucky is home to a large number of horse farms where the Thoroughbred horses that will one day compete in the Derby are bred. In fact, Lexington is the world capital of racehorse breeding. And yes, there *is* more to the state than just horses. There are ponies, too. (Just kidding!) The United States Gold Depository at Fort Knox holds most of the nation's gold reserves. And in the center of the state lies Mammoth Cave. The cave, made up of over 350 miles of passageways below the Earth, is also full of underground lakes, rivers, and even waterfalls.

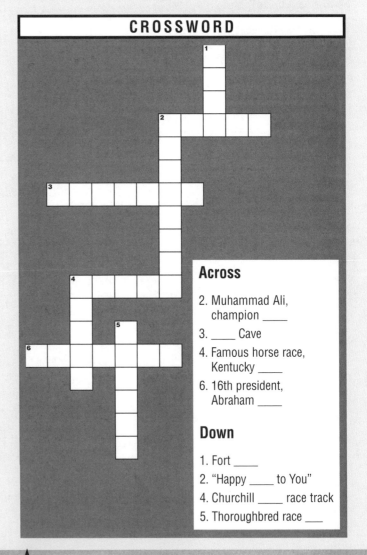

CROSSWORD

Across

2. Muhammad Ali, champion ____

3. ____ Cave

4. Famous horse race, Kentucky ____

6. 16th president, Abraham ____

Down

1. Fort ____

2. "Happy ____ to You"

4. Churchill ____ race track

5. Thoroughbred race ____

How Kentucky Got Its Name

The name is believed by some to have come from the Wyandot Indian word for "plain." Another theory holds that the name was derived from the Cherokee word meaning "land of tomorrow," or "meadow-land." The state is also known as the Bluegrass State, the Hemp State, the Tobacco State, and the Dark and Bloody Ground.

President Born Here!

✪ Abraham Lincoln, 16th President

Historic Site

✪ Abraham Lincoln Birthplace National Historic Site, near Bardstown

State Trivia

✪ Louisville is not only the home of the Kentucky Derby. It's also the birthplace of champion boxer Muhammad Ali, and sisters Mildred and Patty Hill. Never heard of the Hill sisters? You're probably familiar with a little song they wrote, called "Happy Birthday to You."

✪ Is there still a pot of gold at the end? In Cumberland Falls you can see a "moon-bow," a type of rainbow that's only visible at night.

✪ Famed frontiersman Daniel Boone explored and settled much of the wilderness in the state before being taken captive by Native American raiders. Today the Daniel Boone National Forest has over five million visitors every year.

✪ When Abraham Lincoln and Jefferson Davis (the president of the Confederacy) were growing up less than a hundred miles apart in Kentucky, they had no idea that one day they'd be battling each other over the fate of the entire country. The two men were even born within a year of each other!

✪ Another fast food first! Colonel Sanders opened up the original Kentucky Fried Chicken restaurant in Corbin.

WORD SCRAMBLE

neixnglot _____

orghotrdbheu _____

sbeuslarg _____

bnroic _____

oneob _____

bcacoot _____

ogdndoler _____

fotfrrkna _____

Louisiana

DATE OF STATEHOOD:
April 30, 1812

STATE CAPITAL: Baton Rouge

STATE TREE: Bald cypress

STATE FLOWER: Magnolia

STATE BIRD: Brown pelican

The heat is on in Louisiana, where the subtropical climate keeps residents constantly on the alert for tropical storms. However, there's plenty of excitement beyond the threat of the weather. Known as the birthplace of jazz music, New Orleans is full of nonstop activity. During Mardi Gras, parades of people fill the streets in all kinds of wild, fun costumes. The famous Bourbon Street has a full-swing nightlife all year long, and visitors are told not to leave without tasting the delicious local Cajun food.

How Louisiana Got Its Name

Louisiana was named in honor of King Louis XIV of France. The state has many nicknames: the Bayou State, the Sugar State, the Pelican State, the Creole State, Fisherman's Paradise, and the Child of the Mississippi.

State Trivia

✪ The world's longest boxing match, lasting seven hours and nineteen minutes, took place in New Orleans on April 6, 1893.

✪ The city may be known for its music, but the first movie theater—Vitascope Hall—opened in New Orleans on June 26, 1896.

✪ Take cover—Louisiana has a six-month-long hurricane season!

✪ Louisiana is definitely big on spicy food. McIlhenny's Tabasco Company opened shop in the 19th century, producing the first Tabasco sauce.

Baton Rouge

MAZE

Maine

DATE OF STATEHOOD:
March 15, 1820

STATE CAPITAL: Augusta

STATE TREE: White pine

STATE FLOWER: White pine cone and tassel

STATE BIRD: Chickadee

Augusta

Originally belonging to Massachusetts, Maine became its own state in 1820, assuming a distinctive identity. It is the largest New England state, and it has the country's easternmost city: Eastport (that was an easy one to name!). The world's highest tides rise and fall at Passamaquoddy Bay, and visitors to Acadia National Park get to enjoy the only national park in the Northeast. Best of all, anyone who climbs to the top of Mount Katahdin in eastern Maine at the northern end of the Appalachian Trail can be the first person in America to watch the sun rise. And history buffs can see the Burnham Tavernin Machias, where Americans plotted the first naval battle of the Revolutionary War.

How Maine Got Its Name

The name might have been honoring the French province of Mayne, or it could have been the explorers' term for a mainland. Maine is also called the Pine Tree State, the Lumber State, the Border State, and Old Dirigo State.

Historic Sites

- Norlands Living History Center, Auburn
- York Village, York
- Arnold Trail (named for Benedict Arnold *before* he became a traitor.)

State Trivia

- The old "Gaol" (jail) in York used to serve the entire state with its single cell, before being enlarged in 1720. There obviously wasn't any problem with overcrowded jails back then!

- Nearly 90 percent of the nation's supply of lobster comes from Maine, which is why you'll often see "Maine lobster" on a menu, instead of just "lobster."

- Maine is the only state to have its own cat—the Maine Coon Cat. It's also the only state to share a border with only one other state, *and* the only state with a one syllable name.

- Best-selling author Stephen King was born in Portland, and he's set numerous books in his beloved home state.

- Thanks Chester! Young inventor Chester Greenwood of Farmington made the first set of earmuffs in 1873 at age 15.

- Afraid of the dark? Have no fear—there are more lighthouses along the coast of Maine than any other state!

Maryland

DATE OF STATEHOOD:
April 28, 1788

STATE CAPITAL: Annapolis

STATE TREE: White oak

STATE FLOWER: Black-eyed susan

STATE BIRD: Oriole (or Baltimore oriole)

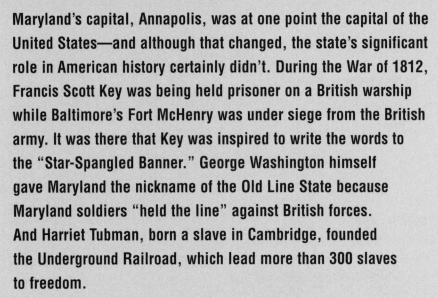

Maryland's capital, Annapolis, was at one point the capital of the United States—and although that changed, the state's significant role in American history certainly didn't. During the War of 1812, Francis Scott Key was being held prisoner on a British warship while Baltimore's Fort McHenry was under siege from the British army. It was there that Key was inspired to write the words to the "Star-Spangled Banner." George Washington himself gave Maryland the nickname of the Old Line State because Maryland soldiers "held the line" against British forces. And Harriet Tubman, born a slave in Cambridge, founded the Underground Railroad, which lead more than 300 slaves to freedom.

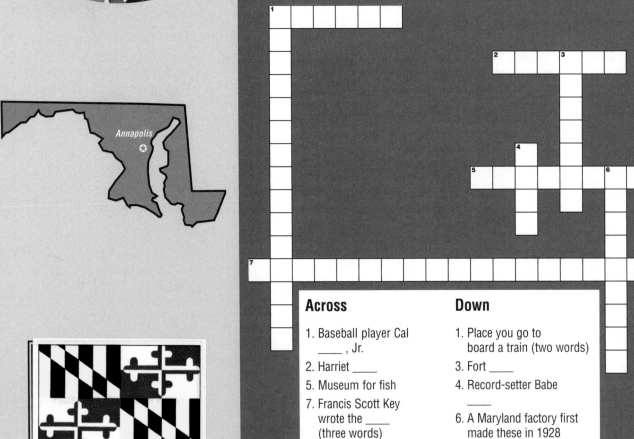

CROSSWORD

Across

1. Baseball player Cal ____ , Jr.
2. Harriet ____
5. Museum for fish
7. Francis Scott Key wrote the ____ (three words)

Down

1. Place you go to board a train (two words)
3. Fort ____
4. Record-setter Babe ____
6. A Maryland factory first made these in 1928

How Maryland Got Its Name

Lord Baltimore gave Maryland its name in honor of Queen Henrietta Maria (known as Queen Mary), the wife of King Charles I of England. Maryland's nicknames include the Old Line State, the Free State, and the Pine Tree State.

Historic Site

✪ Fort McHenry National Monument

State Trivia:

✪ The oldest ship still afloat, the U.S. Frigate *Constellation,* is docked in Baltimore's popular inner harbor.

✪ Maryland is the birthplace of two baseball greats: Babe Ruth and Cal Ripken, Jr. Ruth once held the record for most home runs in a career (714), and Ripken is known for his record-breaking streak—he played in 2,632 consecutive games. He finally chose to sit out for the final game of the 1998 season.

✪ The country's first railroad station for passengers was built in Baltimore in 1830 by the Ohio Railroad Company, and the first umbrella factory opened in Baltimore almost a century later, in 1928.

✪ Slender little Maryland! The state has the narrowest width of any in the country.

✪ The National Aquarium, the largest in the nation, can be found in Baltimore.

✪ Garrett Park is a place of peace. In 1898 it became illegal to harm any tree or songbird within the town's limits. Later, in 1982, Garrett Park declared the nation's first nuclear-free zone. Hopefully the rest of the world will follow the lead soon!

MAZE

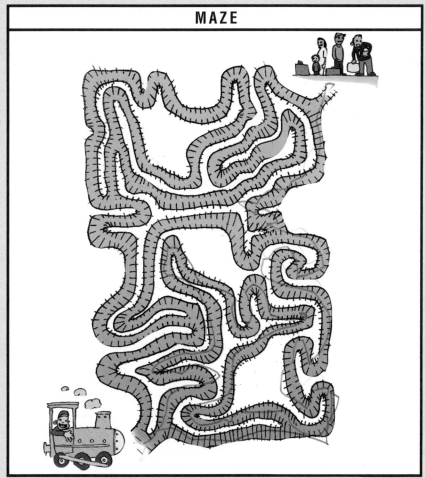

Massachusetts

DATE OF STATEHOOD:
February 6, 1788

STATE CAPITAL: Boston

STATE TREE: American elm

STATE FLOWER: Mayflower

STATE BIRD: Chickadee

It's not surprising that a state with the first printing press (in 1847), the first large municipal public library (in 1852), the first public school system (founded in 1647), and the first college (Harvard—founded in 1636) would also be the birthplace of so many of our country's great minds. Four presidents are Massachusetts natives: John Adams, his son John Quincy Adams, John F. Kennedy, and George H.W. Bush. Ben Franklin—patriot, writer, scientist, inventor, and all-around Renaissance man— was born in Boston. And writers Ralph Waldo Emerson, Nathaniel Hawthorne, Emily Dickinson, e. e. cummings, and Theodore Geisel (Dr. Seuss) all called Massachusetts home. Even before these impressive people were born, Massachusetts had a leading role in our history. When the pilgrims first reached American in 1620, they stepped onto Plymouth Rock. And the Revolutionary War began here on April 19, 1775, with the "shot heard around the world."

Boston

WORD SCRAMBLE

vhdrara _____

siterwr _____

mypluoht korc _____

tebkalbals _____

nbtsoo eat ptray _____

oylvellabl _____

igf wtenno _____

lupa ervere _____

How Massachusetts Got Its Name

The name comes from a Massachuset Indian word meaning "large hill place," because of the Great Blue Hill, located south of the town of Milton. Massachusetts is also known as the Baked Bean State, the Old Colony State, the Bay State, the Old Bay State, the Pilgrim State, and the Puritan State.

Presidents Born Here!

☉ John Adams, 2nd president

☉ John Quincy Adams, 6th president

☉ John Fitzgerald Kennedy, 35th president

☉ George H.W. Bush, 41st president

Historic Site

☉ Paul Revere's House, Boston

State Trivia

☉ A state of hoop dreams! Basketball was invented by James Naismith in Springfield in 1891. The first game was played the following year, and the city is now home to the Basketball Hall of Fame.

☉ Along with basketball, Massachusetts is also responsible for volleyball, which was invented at the Holyoke YMCA in 1895.

☉ Visit Rockport to see a house built *entirely* of newspaper!

☉ Massachusetts hosted the first World Series in 1903. The teams playing? The Boston Pilgrims (!) and the Pittsburgh Pirates.

☉ Alexander Graham Bell invented the first telephone in Boston in 1876, and the city also built the first subway system in America in 1897.

☉ The popular Fig Newton dessert was named after Newton, Massachusetts. But the *official* state dessert is still Boston Cream Pie. *There's* a good reason to take a trip there!

CROSSWORD

Across

2. Massachusetts state capital
4. _____ War
6. Printing _____
8. "_____ heard around the world"

Down

1. Where you go to borrow books
3. Beloved children's writer, Dr. _____
5. Alexander Graham Bell invented the _____
7. Baseball's championship is called the World _____

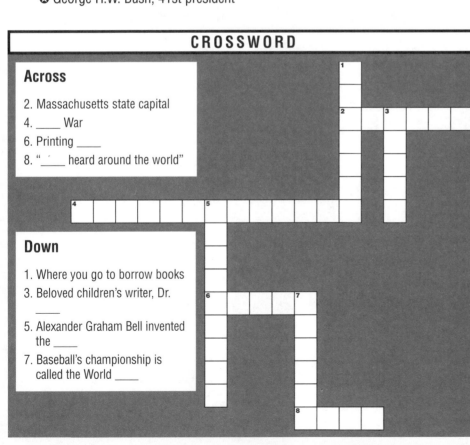

Michigan

DATE OF STATEHOOD:
January 26, 1837

STATE CAPITAL: Lansing

STATE TREE: White pine

STATE FLOWER: Apple blossom

STATE BIRD: Robin

Olds Motor Works, the first U.S. auto factory, was founded in Detroit in 1900, leading to the development of an industry that would forever change the state of Michigan, as well as the rest of the country. (Can you imagine if we were still traveling around by horse and buggy? There could never have been any drive-in movie theaters!) Henry Ford, opening his Ford Motor Company in 1903, revolutionized the process of manufacturing cars so that typical citizens could afford to buy them. Automobiles have been hot products on the market ever since—and today, Detroit produces over one quarter of the nation's autos, trucks, and tractors. Michigan's Motor City was home to another source of pride for the state: the Motown record label, which produced records from many big names in music, including Smoky Robinson and the Temptations. Today, the Motown Museum in Motor City gives visitors the chance to see how it all began.

How Michigan Got Its Name

The name comes from the word *majigan,* which is a Chippewa Indian term meaning "clearing." The word refers to a place on the west side of the lower peninsula. Michigan is also called the Wolverine State, the Great Lakes State, the Lake State, the Lady of the Lake, and the Auto State.

State Trivia

✪ Abracadabra! The world's largest manufacturer of magic supplies is located in Colon, and in Marshall you can visit the American Museum of Magic.

✪ Despite its nickname as the Wolverine State, there are no longer any wolverines in Michigan. (Oh well!)

Historic Site

✪ Greenfield Village, Dearborn— built by Henry Ford. The park has a model of Thomas Edison's laboratory and the Wright brothers' bicycle shop.

CROSSWORD

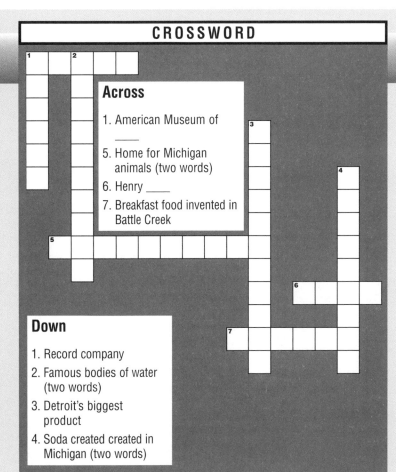

Across

1. American Museum of
____
5. Home for Michigan
animals (two words)
6. Henry ____
7. Breakfast food invented in
Battle Creek

Down

1. Record company
2. Famous bodies of water
(two words)
3. Detroit's biggest
product
4. Soda created created in
Michigan (two words)

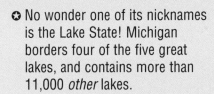 No wonder one of its nicknames is the Lake State! Michigan borders four of the five great lakes, and contains more than 11,000 *other* lakes.

✪ The Detroit Zoo was the first in American to have open exhibits, where animals aren't held in cages.

✪ Ginger ale, the first soda pop made in the United States, was created in Michigan by pharmacist James Vernor.

✪ Michigan is the only contiguous state where Canada is *south* of America!

MAZE

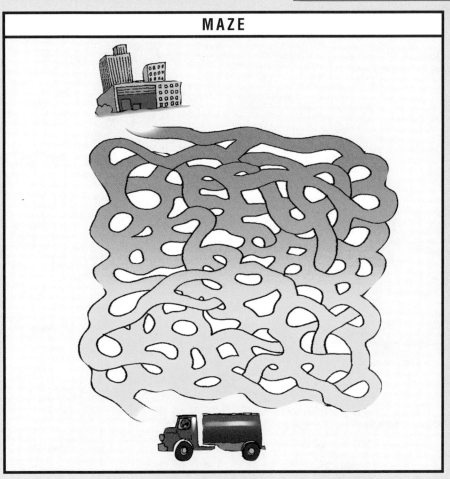

✪ Two halls of fame are located here: The Afro-American Sports Hall of Fame is in Detroit, and the National Ski Hall of Fame can be found in Ishpeming.

✪ Battle Creek is known as the Cereal Capital of the World because the Kellogg Company invented dry cereal here— by accident!

✪ The only floating post office in existence (it's on a boat, of course!) can be found in this state.

✪ In 1929, Michigan State Police became the first in the world to use a police radio system.

Minnesota

DATE OF STATEHOOD:
May 11, 1858

STATE CAPITAL: St. Paul

STATE TREE: Norway pine
(red pine)

STATE FLOWER: Pink and white
lady's slipper

STATE BIRD: Common loon

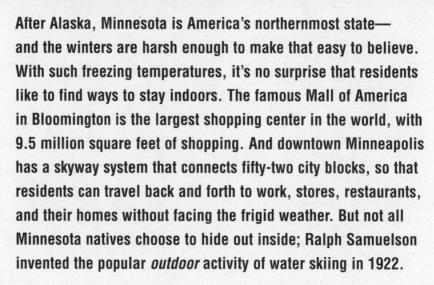

After Alaska, Minnesota is America's northernmost state—and the winters are harsh enough to make that easy to believe. With such freezing temperatures, it's no surprise that residents like to find ways to stay indoors. The famous Mall of America in Bloomington is the largest shopping center in the world, with 9.5 million square feet of shopping. And downtown Minneapolis has a skyway system that connects fifty-two city blocks, so that residents can travel back and forth to work, stores, restaurants, and their homes without facing the frigid weather. But not all Minnesota natives choose to hide out inside; Ralph Samuelson invented the popular *outdoor* activity of water skiing in 1922.

St. Paul

How Minnesota Got Its Name

The name is derived from the Dakota Indian word *mnishota*, which means "cloudy" or "milky water," referring to the Minnesota River. Minnesota is also called the North Star State, the Gopher State, the Land of Ten Thousand Lakes, and the Bread and Butter State.

State Trivia

✪ There are so many lakes—over 22,000—that many share the same name, because they ran out of choices!

✪ The Metrodome sports center has hosted the Super Bowl, the World Series, *and* the NCAA college basketball championship.

✪ The U.S. Hockey Hall of Fame is located in Eveleth—probably because Minnesota's a state that can appreciate an icy sport!

✪ The oldest rock in the world was found in Minnesota River Valley. How ancient? 3.8 billion years old!

✪ *Peanuts* cartoonist Charles Schulz, who brought Charlie Brown into the world and into our hearts, was born in Minneapolis in 1922.

✪ Some very important office supplies—masking tape, scotch tape, and the stapler—were all invented in Minnesota. (Guess they really *do* spend a lot of time indoors here!)

✪ Residents of St. Paul almost had to say they were from "Pig's Eye," which was the original name of the capital. French-Canadian trader Pierre Parrant, who established the city in 1840, named it after his own nickname. But in 1841, the settlers were convinced to change the name to St. Paul. Talk about a lucky break!

Mississippi

DATE OF STATEHOOD:
December 10, 1817

STATE CAPITAL: Jackson

STATE TREE: Evergreen magnolia

STATE FLOWER: Evergreen magnolia

STATE BIRD: Mockingbird

Jackson

What could be more American than football, Coca-Cola, and Elvis Presley? The first football player to go on a Wheaties cereal box was Walter Payton of Columbia, and Coca-Cola— the enduringly popular soft drink—was first bottled in Vicksburg in 1894. Elvis Presley, the "king" of rock and roll, was born in Tupelo in 1935. Another famous Mississippi native? Muppets creator Jim Henson, who brought Kermit the Frog and Miss Piggy to life.

How Mississippi Got Its Name

Referring to the Mississippi River, the name comes from the Chippewa Indian word meaning "large river." Mississippi is also known as the Magnolia State, the Eagle State, the Border-Eagle State, the Bayou State, and the Mud-Cat State.

Historic Sites

- Florewood River Plantation, Greenwood
- John Ford House, near Sandy Hook—early 1800s frontier home

State Trivia

- In 1902, Theodore (also known as Teddy) Roosevelt was visiting Sharkey County when he refused to shoot a bear being held in captivity. The adorable teddy bear was created in honor of this act.

- Yes, they actually have one—the International Checkers Hall of Fame can be found in Petal.

- Dr. James D. Hardy performed the first heart transplant at the University of Mississippi Medical Center in Jackson in 1964. He transplanted a heart from a chimpanzee into a human!

- How convenient! The state flower here is the blossom of the state tree.

- If someone tells you to listen to the Pascagoula River "sing," it's not a joke! The river does make sounds very similar to a song.

- The delicious Mississippi Mud Cake was named after the Mississippi Delta's rich, dark mud. The cake may resemble the Delta, but it definitely doesn't taste like it!

Missouri

DATE OF STATEHOOD:
August 10, 1821

STATE CAPITAL: Jefferson City

STATE TREE: Flowering dogwood

STATE FLOWER: Hawthorn

STATE BIRD: Bluebird

Missouri's St. Louis is really an exciting place! The first World's Fair, held there in 1904, is credited for the invention of several tasty treats. Tea was served with ice, leading to the creation of iced tea, and ice cream cones were supposedly first enjoyed. St. Louis is also home to the tallest monument: the Gateway Arch, reaching 630 feet high—and to two halls of fame: the National Bowling Hall of Fame, and the St. Louis Sports Hall of Fame. Finally, President Warren Harding gave the first presidential radio broadcast from St. Louis University in 1921!

How Missouri Got Its Name

The state was named after the Missouri River, which was originally named after the Missouri Indian word for "canoe possessor." Missouri is also called the Show Me State, the Bullion State, the Cave State, the Lead State, and the Ozark State.

President Born Here!

✪ Harry S. Truman, 33rd president

Historic Sites

✪ Benjamin Ranch, Kansas City

✪ Bequette-Ribault Living History Museum

State Trivia

✪ St. Joseph was the start point of the old pony express in 1860, where relay teams would carry mail to San Francisco in ten days, at great risk to their lives.

✪ Warsaw holds the state record for lowest *and* highest temperatures. In 1905 it went all the way down to −40 degrees F, and then in 1954 it reached 118 degrees F!

✪ Writers Mark Twain and Langston Hughes were both Missouri natives. Mark Twain was born in Hannibal in 1835, and Langston Hughes was born in Joplin in 1902.

✪ Missouri gets an average of twenty-five to thirty tornadoes every year!

✪ Where do all those greeting cards come from? Hallmark Cards, Inc. has its headquarters in Kansas City.

Jefferson City

Montana

DATE OF STATEHOOD:
November 8, 1889

STATE CAPITAL: Helena

STATE TREE: Ponderosa pine

STATE FLOWER: Bitterroot

STATE BIRD: Western meadowlark

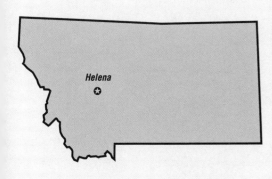

Helena ✪

Montana's most fascinating natural feature is the Continental Divide. The Divide literally separates the state into two different geographical regions. To the east, rivers flow toward the Atlantic Ocean, while rivers to the west flow toward the Pacific Ocean. Looking westward, you see tall Rocky Mountains, but the east is made up of broad, flat plains. (Talk about a state with a split personality!) Earthquake Lake, another one of nature's creations, was produced when a mountainside collapsed across the Madison River during the August 17, 1959, earthquake. One of the least populous states, Montana's elk, deer, and antelope populations actually *outnumber* humans.

How Montana Got Its Name

Montana comes from the Spanish word *montana,* meaning "mountainous." The state is also known as Big Sky Country, the Mountain State, the Stub Toe State (ouch!), the Bonanza State, and the Treasure State.

State Trivia

✪ Known as the Treasure State, Montana has the only sapphire mines in the United States, along with gold and silver mines.

✪ Before Montana was a state, the area was part of five different territories. One family lived in a house on the borders, and so the four brothers born there were each born in separate territories!

✪ Chicago may be nicknamed the Windy City, but Great Falls is really the windiest city in the United States. The wind here blows 13.1 miles per hour on average.

✪ Fossils of the dangerous Tyrannosaurus Rex have been found only in Montana. Maybe that's why so few people live there!

✪ Grasshopper Glacier is named after the grasshoppers that can still be seen frozen in the ice!

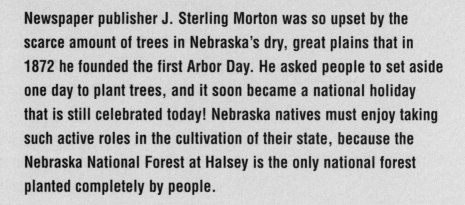

Nebraska

DATE OF STATEHOOD:
March 1, 1867

STATE CAPITAL: Lincoln

STATE TREE: Cottonwood

STATE FLOWER: Late goldenrod

STATE BIRD: Western meadowlark

Newspaper publisher J. Sterling Morton was so upset by the scarce amount of trees in Nebraska's dry, great plains that in 1872 he founded the first Arbor Day. He asked people to set aside one day to plant trees, and it soon became a national holiday that is still celebrated today! Nebraska natives must enjoy taking such active roles in the cultivation of their state, because the Nebraska National Forest at Halsey is the only national forest planted completely by people.

How Nebraska Got Its Name

The name comes from the Omaha Indian name for the Platte River, *niboathka,* meaning "broad river." Nebraska's official nickname is the Cornhusker State. It's also called the Tree Planters' State, the Antelope State, and the Bug-Eating State.

President Born Here!

✪ Gerald Ford, 38th president

Historic Sites

✪ Pioneer Village, Mindon

✪ Scouts Rest Ranch, North Platte—Buffalo Bill Cody's home and Wild West Show training grounds

State Trivia

✪ What's *your* favorite flavor? Kool-Aid was invented in Hastings by Edwin E. Perkins in 1927.

✪ The world's only Roller Skating Museum is located in Lincoln. (As if there needs to be more than one!)

✪ Actor Marlon Brando was born in Omaha, as was African-American leader Malcolm X.

✪ The 911 system of emergency response was first developed and used in this quick-thinking state.

✪ Why is Nebraska the Bug-Eating State?" Because there are so many insect-eating bull bats here! (Yuck!)

Nevada

DATE OF STATEHOOD:
October 31, 1864

STATE CAPITAL: Carson City

STATE TREE: Single-leaf piñon

STATE FLOWER: Sagebrush

STATE BIRD: Mountain bluebird

Nevada, made up primarily of desert, gets less rain than any other state. It's too dry to farm here, so the land is used mostly to graze cattle, horses, and sheep. However, the city of Las Vegas is booming with people and activity. There are more hotel rooms here than in any other place on Earth; in fact, tourists alone outnumber the entire populations of several other states! Visitors come to gamble at one of the numerous local casinos, check out the 61-pound solid gold nugget at the Gold Nugget Casino, or visit the Guinness World of Records Museum.

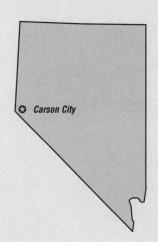

Carson City

How Nevada Got Its Name

Nevada comes from the Spanish word meaning "snowy" or "snow-capped." Nicknames for the state include the Sage State, the Sagebrush State, the Silver State, the Mining State, and the Battle Born State.

State Trivia

✪ Virginia City, an old mining town that was once full of people during the gold rush in 1859, now hosts the International Camel Races. Guess things have slowed down a little here, huh?

✪ Though known for its desert, Nevada actually has more mountain ranges than any other state.

✪ The Imperial Palace Auto collection in Las Vegas has more than 300 antique cars, many once owned by famous people!

✪ No, the Extraterrestrial Highway *won't* take you up to another planet to meet aliens! Route 375 was actually given that name because it passes the United States military base called Area 51, where UFO sightings have been reported.

✪ Nevada is a top producer of gold, turquoise, and rare opals. What a pretty combo!

✪ Reno, another popular gambling city, is known as the Biggest Little City in the World.

✪ Roughly 225 million years ago, the land that now makes up central Nevada was covered in warm ocean. Fossils of ichthyosaurs, the marine reptiles that once swam in that ocean, can be seen today in the Berlin-Ichthyosaur State Park.

✪ The hard hats that you see on construction workers everywhere these days weren't always a regular part of the job. The hats were originally invented for workers building the Hoover Dam here in 1933.

New Hampshire

DATE OF STATEHOOD:
June 21, 1788

STATE CAPITAL: Concord

STATE TREE: White birch

STATE FLOWER: Purple lilac

STATE BIRD: Purple finch

New Hampshire, the first of the original thirteen colonies to declare independence from Great Britain, is truly a patriotic state. In fact, the United States could not form an official union until New Hampshire became the ninth state to sign the Constitution! Since the year 1952, the nation's first official presidential primary has always been held in New Hampshire. And the state legislature, with 400 members, is the largest in the country. But the state is not only about politics. It's also home to the highest peak in New England, Mt. Washington—6,288 feet tall—and to a real natural wonder, the 40-foot rock Franconia Rock—nicknamed Old Man of the Mountains because of its extraordinary resemblance to the profile of a man's head. Freaky!

Concord

CROSSWORD

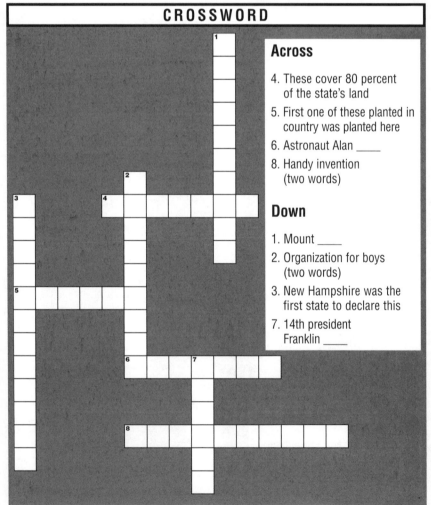

Across

4. These cover 80 percent of the state's land
5. First one of these planted in country was planted here
6. Astronaut Alan ____
8. Handy invention (two words)

Down

1. Mount ____
2. Organization for boys (two words)
3. New Hampshire was the first state to declare this
7. 14th president Franklin ____

How New Hampshire Got Its Name

John Mason named the state for the county of Hampshire in England. New Hampshire is also known as the Granite State, the White Mountain State, the Switzerland of America, and the Mother of Rivers.

President Born Here!

✪ Franklin Pierce, 14th president

Historic Sites

✪ America's Stonehenge, Salem

✪ Six Gun City, Jefferson

✪ Strawberry Banke, Portsmouth—with buildings from 1695 to 1820

✪ Canterbury Shaker Village, Concord

State Trivia

✪ Remember—always be prepared! The Lawrence L. Lee Scouting Museum in Merrimack Valley is packed with history about the Boy Scouts of America.

✪ The peace treaty ending the Russo-Japanese War was signed in Portsmouth on September 5, 1905.

✪ Good idea or bad? It's still undecided—Concord resident Levi Hutchins invented the alarm clock in 1787. (At least it has a snooze button, right?)

✪ Alan Shepard, the first American to travel in space and also the fifth man to walk on the moon, was born in East Derry in 1923.

✪ Forget Idaho! The first potato planted in the United States was at Londonderry Common Field in 1719.

✪ Artificial rain was first used in New Hampshire in 1947 to fight a forest fire. Forests actually cover 80 percent of the territory in the state.

✪ Mt. Washington is not only the tallest peak in New England, it also has the highest wind velocity in the United States—the wind averages 35.2 miles an hour. That's how fast *cars* drive on most side roads!

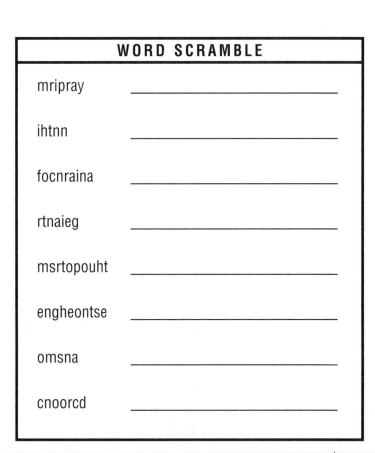

```
WORD SCRAMBLE

mripray      _____

ihtnn        _____

focnraina    _____

rtnaieg      _____

msrtopouht   _____

engheontse   _____

omsna        _____

cnoorcd      _____
```

New Jersey

DATE OF STATEHOOD:
December 18, 1787

STATE CAPITAL: Trenton

STATE TREE: Northern red oak and dogwood

STATE FLOWER: Meadow violet

STATE BIRD: Eastern goldfinch

Trenton

New Jersey is definitely a state that knows how to have fun—from the beaches along the Jersey shore to all the activity in the urban cities. Need some proof? The world's first professional baseball game was held in Hoboken in 1846, and the first drive-in movie theater opened in Camden. Ever since 1921, the Miss America contest has been held annually in exciting Atlantic City—home to the longest boardwalk in the world. Every summer, marble loyalists gather in Wildwood for the National Marbles Tournament. And if you're looking for new hangouts, New Jersey has the world's most diners and shopping centers. Convinced yet?

How New Jersey Got Its Name

Sir John Berkeley and Sir George Carteret named the state after the English Channel island of Jersey. New Jersey's nicknames include the Garden State, the Clam State, the Camden and Amboy State, the Jersey Blue State, and the Pathway of the Revolution.

President Born Here!

⊕ Grover Cleveland, 22nd & 24th president (He couldn't stay away!)

Historic Sites:

⊕ Batsto—a colonial village,

⊕ Clinton Historical Museum Village, Clinton

⊕ Historic Cold Springs Village,

⊕ Cape May—with preserved Victorian houses

⊕ Waterloo Village Restoration, Stanhope

⊕ Washington Crossing State Park, Titusville

State Trivia

⊕ Until 1916, New Jersey was the movie capital that Hollywood is today. Thomas A. Edison developed the light bulb and motion picture projector—inventions that made moviemaking possible—in his lab at Menlo Park. Now California has the movies and celebrities, but New Jersey still has all those malls and diners!

⊕ Along with Edison, another brilliant mind did his research here—Albert Einstein worked at Princeton University in Princeton.

CROSSWORD

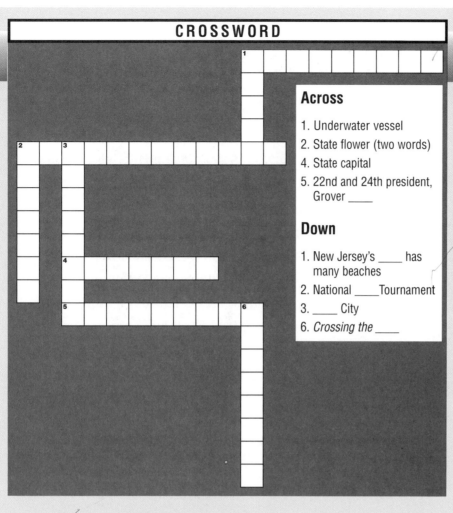

Across

1. Underwater vessel
2. State flower (two words)
4. State capital
5. 22nd and 24th president, Grover _____

Down

1. New Jersey's _____ has many beaches
2. National _____ Tournament
3. _____ City
6. *Crossing the _____*

✪ Today Camden has the Campbell's Soup headquarters (mmm mmm good!), and the city was once home to great American poet Walt Whitman.

✪ The famous painting *Washington Crossing the Delaware* depicts Christmas night 1776 when General George Washington and his troops crossed the icy river into Trenton. Never seen it? Check out the scene on New Jersey's state quarter!

✪ John P. Holland, inventor of the submarine, took the first ride in his creation in the Passaic River.

✪ Where can you find the *real* Park Place and Board Walk? The street names for the popular board game Monopoly come from Atlantic City!

✪ The Boy Scouts of America headquarters are located in New Brunswick.

WORD SCRAMBLE

wbdraklao   _____

ebsalabl   _____

msis mreaiac _____

dneois   _____

csalmlpeb   _____

tnsieien   _____

edinsr   _____

oby ctsuos   _____

New Mexico

DATE OF STATEHOOD:
January 6, 1912

STATE CAPITAL: Santa Fe

STATE TREE: Piñon

STATE FLOWER: Yucca flower

STATE BIRD: Roadrunner

Known as the Spanish State, New Mexico remains the state with the most surviving evidence of the Spanish, Mexican, and Native American cultures that once populated the area. The Navajo reservation, where the largest Native American group in the United States lives, stretches over New Mexico's borders to neighboring states Arizona and Utah. The oldest house in America can be found in New Mexico (hopefully they've redecorated by now!), and so can the nation's first road—El Camino Real, which takes you from Santa Fe down to Chihuahua, Mexico. Billy the Kid, the famous young outlaw, spent his days in this state, possibly exploring some of the caves, ruins, and cliff dwellings left by the different peoples who used to inhabit the land.

Santa Fe
✪

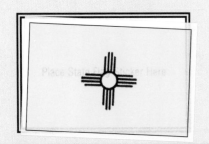

CROSSWORD

Across

2. New Mexico's capital (two words)
3. Famous outlaw (three words)
4. Unique crop (two words)
6. ____ Caverns

Down

1. ____ Bear
2. International ____ Hall of Fame
4. Hot air ____
5. ____ Reservation

How New Mexico Got Its Name

This one's simple—the name came from the country of Mexico! Spanish explorers were calling the state *Nuevo Mexico* (literally—New Mexico) as early as 1561. New Mexico is also known as the Land of Enchantment, the Cactus State, and the Spanish State.

Historic Sites

- Puye Cliff Dwellings, Santa Clara Pueblo—740-room indian structure

- Palace of Governors, Santa Fe—oldest government building in United States

- White Sands National Monument—desert of gleaming white gypsum crystals

State Trivia:

- Albuquerque is known for its hot air balloon rides. And every October, the city hosts the world's largest International Hot Air Balloon Fiesta.

- Smokey Bear Historical State Park was named for a *real* bear. Little Smokey was rescued from a forest fire as a cub, and the park was later named for him.

- If you're already in town for the Balloon Fiesta in October, then stop by Las Cruces the first weekend of the month for the Whole Enchilada Fiesta, where the world's largest enchiladas are made!

- Blue corn grows around Albuquerque and Santa Fe, making New Mexico the only state to produce this special crop.

- The International Space Hall of Fame, located in Alamagordo, has real moon rocks!

- The city of Roswell became world famous after 1947, when "evidence" emerged of a supposed UFO crash here. It's never been proved . . . but plenty of books, movies, and television series have been based on the idea that it really happened!

- Carlsbad Caverns has 77 underground caverns, including the world's largest underground room—more than ten football fields long and about twenty-two stories high! Most rooms aren't open to the public, but the ones that are offer amazing sights. Just be careful if you're near here at night, when millions of bats usually fly out of the cave opening!

MAZE

New York

DATE OF STATEHOOD:
July 26, 1788

STATE CAPITAL: Albany

STATE TREE: Sugar maple

STATE FLOWER: Rose

STATE BIRD: Bluebird

"If I can make it there, I'll make it anywhere." Where was Frank Sinatra singing about? New York City, of course! It may not be the capital of American any more (it was for a short time after the Revolutionary War), but many would say it's our country's most popular city. Full of museums, Broadway theaters, restaurants, and much more, New York is a city that doesn't disappoint. Roughly three out of every four of our nation's books are published in New York, where the publishing industry booms. Sightseers can feast their eyes on the Empire State Building, the World Trade Center towers, the Brooklyn Bridge, and even the largest department store in the country—the original Macy's. In New York Harbor are Ellis Island and the Statue of Liberty, two big tourist treats. It's often hard to remember that New York State has more to it than just this exciting city, but traveling upstate you can find the Catskills and the Adirondacks—beautiful mountain ranges—and the awe-inspiring Niagara Falls, shared with Canada.

How New York Got Its Name

The state was named to honor the Duke of York and Albany. New York's official nickname is the Empire State, but it is also called the Excelsior State, and the Knickerbocker State.

Presidents Born Here!

✪ Martin Van Buren, 8th president

✪ Millard Fillmore, 13th president

✪ Theodore Roosevelt, 26th president

✪ Franklin Delano Roosevelt, 32nd president

Historic Sites

✪ Niagara Falls

✪ Statue of Liberty

State Trivia

✪ New York has—get ready for this—*six* halls of fame: the Baseball Hall of Fame in Cooperstown, the Boxing Hall of Fame in Canastota, the Hall of Fame for Great Americans in the Bronx, the National Women's Hall of Fame in Seneca Falls, the Soccer Hall of Fame in Oneonta, and the Speed Skating Hall of Fame in Newburgh. (Try enough different hobbies, and you'll have a good shot at making it into one of these, right?)

CROSSWORD

Across

1. Popular Waterfall
4. Strategic board game
6. Writer, Washington
   ———
7. You have one of these in your hands right now!

Down

1. The Big Apple (three words
2. Where immigrants once entered America (two words)
3. Joseph C. Gayetty's invention (two words
5. Method of public transportation

✪ Checkmate! The first American chess tournament was held in New York in 1843.

✪ Have you ever been on a New York City subway? If you've visited the city, chances are you have, so you won't be too surprised to learn that there are a full 722 miles of subway track!

WORD SEARCH

```
A T C N R H S C I U T S I L B Z B N U B
J I L S E O Z E P R S Y C A M U N A S S
S N W O V S F I E T K H J L Q I Q T D P
C A A R E S T A U R A N T S F W N Y N C
T U Y J I Y U J N E R G N I W W B L P U
K G W C P E R C N D R S B U O M K E T M
G U B T Z N M G X K W G T T H W A Y U L
Y R X S C A T S K I L L S V E G P S J V
D A H M V H N U H K W R M S I S E U E A
T T M V R A M C R O E Q R A J U D P R I
F I R D O O P K I P U B D R M S L C F T
M O Y L O N D S O L W Y N S E P F N O L
R N K S S M X O B W D T F H G T E J V D
B M F A E T C Q C S G R C H K L B M Y Y
V P U S V F P U J Y E J Y A P I V F Z T
K E N V E B H E I E M P I R E D T T O R
I V O W L A G R W F O Z M L W O M D L E
H B L E T K F L A J K V D X G N R Y N B
O S N K N I C K E R B O C K E R E R T I
E L F K R C H V O L A P X J V O T C K L
```

WORDS	Empire	Liberty	Restaurants
Catskills	Inauguration	Macys	Roosevelt
Cooperstown	Knickerbocker	Museums	

✪ Can you imagine life without toilet paper? It wasn't invented until 1857, when New York City's Joseph C. Gayetty came up with the brilliant idea.

✪ The first presidential inauguration, of (who else?) George Washington took place in New York City in 1789.

✪ Another upstate landmark is Sunnyside, writer Washington Irving's estate. While he lived there, he wrote the creepy tales *The Legend of Sleepy Hollow* and *Rip Van Winkle*.

✪ Here's a new one: Wellsville holds an Inner Tube Regatta every Memorial Day weekend. Yep—an *inner tube race*. Wouldn't you like to see that?

North Carolina

DATE OF STATEHOOD:
November 21, 1789

STATE CAPITAL: Raleigh

STATE TREE: Longleafed pine
(southern pine)

STATE FLOWER: Dogwood

STATE BIRD: Cardinal

North Carolina, the twelfth state to enter the union, has a rich history of impressive accomplishments and fascinating legends. The University of North Carolina at Chapel Hill is the oldest state university in the country, and the Wright brothers first developed an airplane that worked at Kitty Hawk, where there is now a museum and national memorial in their honor. As for mystery and myth, Beaufort was home to the great pirate Blackbeard, and the area on Roanoke Island now known as the Lost Colony was once the first English colony—until it disappeared several years later!

How North Carolina Got Its Name

The state was originally named in honor of King Charles IX of France, and then later for King Charles I and King Charles II of England. North Carolina is also called the Tar Heel State, the Old North State, and the Turpentine State.

Presidents Born Here!

✪ James K. Polk, 11th president

✪ Andrew Johnson, 17th president

Historic Sites

✪ Andrew Johnson Birthplace, Raleigh

✪ James K. Polk Birthplace, Pineville

State Trivia

✪ Don't raise your voice anywhere else in the state—it used to be illegal to sing out of tune here!

✪ Feel like letting loose? Travel to Spivey's Corner for the National Hollerin' Contest.

✪ North Carolina even has a hall of fame—the PGA/World Golf Hall of Fame is in Pinehurst.

✪ At 193 feet high, the lighthouse at Cape Hatteras ranks as the world's tallest.

✪ North Carolina's official nickname is actually an insult! During the Civil War, when North Carolina Confederate troops were chased from their position by Union troops, Mississippi Confederate soldiers said it was because the North Carolinians had forgotten to "tar their heels" so they would stick their ground.

North Dakota

DATE OF STATEHOOD: November 2, 1889

STATE CAPITAL: Bismarck

STATE TREE: American elm

STATE FLOWER: Wild prairie rose

STATE BIRD: Meadowlark

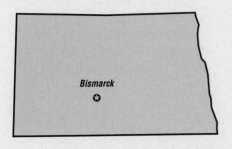

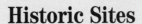

Bismarck

Here's the big question: is North Dakota the thirty-ninth or fortieth state? President Benjamin Harrison signed both North and South Dakota's statehood bills on the same day, and no one knows which came first. Another unknown is how long the state's coal bed's underground fires have been burning. It's been so long that nobody's even sure what caused the fires. But we do know that the geographical center of North America is located in Rugby, and the world's tallest structure—a 2,063-foot-tall television transmission tower—can be found in Blanchard.

How North Dakota Got Its Name

The name comes from the Dakota Indian word meaning "friends," or "allies." The state's official nicknames are the Sioux State and the Flickertail State. Others include the Land of the Dakotas and the Peace Garden State.

Historic Sites

✪ Fort Union Trading Post

✪ Knife River Indian Villages, Stanton

✪ Fort Buford, where Sioux leader Sitting Bull was once imprisoned

State Trivia:

✪ The world's largest buffalo statue is in Jamestown, standing 26 feet tall and weighing in at 60 tons. Over in New Salem resides a 38-foot Holstein cow statue called Salem Sue. If only they were a little closer, they could keep each other company!

✪ Baseball great Roger Maris, who broke Babe Ruth's record for home runs in one season with 61 runs total, was a North Dakota native.

✪ Golfers at the Portal golf course sometimes watch their balls cross country borders, since the course extends into Canada!

✪ The Lewis and Clark Historic Trail honors the explorer pair who once traveled this area and stayed here in winters.

✪ In 1982 Rutland was responsible for a Guinness Record–breaking burger. The 3,501 pound hamburger was cooked there, and more than 8,000 people came to eat it. (Bet they weren't feeling too good later!)

Ohio

DATE OF STATEHOOD:
March 1, 1803

STATE CAPITAL: Columbus

STATE TREE: Buckeye

STATE FLOWER: Scarlet carnation

STATE BIRD: Cardinal

Between admirable natives and important firsts, Ohio has a lot to be proud of! A total of seven presidents were born here, along with the accomplished writer Toni Morrison, the inventor Thomas Edison, and film director Steven Spielberg. Another hometown heroine was Judith Resnick. One of the first female astronauts, Resnick was sadly killed in the *Challenger* shuttle explosion. On a brighter note, Oberlin was the first U.S. college to enroll both men and women. The Cincinnati Reds were the first professional baseball team, and Akron was the first city to use police cars!

How Ohio Got Its Name

The state's name comes from the Iroquois word *ohio,* meaning "beautiful river" or "large river." Ohio is also known as the Buckeye State and the Mother of Modern Presidents.

Presidents Born Here!

- Ulysses S. Grant, 18th president
- Rutherford B. Hayes, 19th president
- James Garfield, 20th president
- Benjamin Harrison, 23rd president
- William McKinley, 25th president
- William Howard Taft, 27th president
- Warren G. Harding, 29th president

Historic Sites

- Adena State Memorial, Chillicothe—1807 stone house
- Gardens of Zoar—1817 settlement where men and women had equal rights (Sad but true—this was actually a big deal back then!)

State Trivia

- Something for everyone! Music lovers can visit the Rock and Roll Hall of Fame in Cleveland, sports buffs can check out the Pro Football Hall of Fame in Canton, and fans of flying get to see the National Aviation Hall of Fame, also in Canton!

- Before starring in Buffalo Bill's wild west show, the famous sharpshooter Annie Oakley probably practiced in her backyard here in her home state.

- Pioneer astronauts Neil Armstrong and John Glenn, Jr. were both born in Ohio, and today the Neil Armstrong Air and Space Museum at Wapakoneta lets anyone who's interested get a glimpse of what they saw out there!

Oklahoma

DATE OF STATEHOOD:
November 16, 1907

STATE CAPITAL: Oklahoma City

STATE TREE: Redbud

STATE FLOWER: Mistletoe

STATE BIRD: Scissor-tailed fly catcher

Cowboy lovers unite—this is your state! There's a cowboy monument in front of Oklahoma City's Capitol building, as well as both a National Cowboy Hall of Fame and a Rodeo Cowboy Hall of Fame located nearby. Also in the capital city, one of the state's many oil wells pumps oil from right under the Capitol building! But it was Tulsa that, in the 1920s, had more millionaires than any other city. The so-called Oil Capital of the World is so rich with this natural resource that some people have even found it in their backyards!

How Oklahoma Got Its Name

The Choctaw Indian words ukla and huma, meaning "person," and "red," were combined to produce Oklahoma's name. The state is also known as the Sooner State and the Boomer State.

Oklahoma City

State Trivia

- Another state with a split personality! Oklahoma has two completely different climates. In the southwest, it's very dry— but it's humid and subtropical in the east.

- The first parking meter was installed in Oklahoma City in 1935.

- Wrestling, sometimes called man's oldest sport, has its National Hall of Fame in Stillwater. Oklahoma also has three other Halls of Fame: The International Photography Hall of Fame and National Softball Hall of Fame are both in Oklahoma City, and the

National Hall of Fame for Famous American Indians is located in Anadarko.

- America's deepest hole is the 31,441-foot-deep natural gas well in Washita County.

- Oklahoma native Sylvan Goldman invented the shopping cart, a true modern convenience. And fellow Oklahoman Clinton Riggs created the first YIELD sign, which was originally used on a trial basis in Tulsa. Obviously it worked, because now you can spot the bright yellow sign all over the country!

OKLAHOMA

Oregon

DATE OF STATEHOOD:
February 14, 1859

STATE CAPITAL: Salem

STATE TREE: Douglas fir

STATE FLOWER: Oregon grape

STATE BIRD: Western meadowlark

Oregon is full of eye-pleasing wonders. Crater Lake, created when the ancient volcano Mount Mazama exploded, is the deepest lake in the United States at 1,932 feet deep. Snake River Canyon is the deepest canyon in the country, and the Oregon Trail the longest overland pioneer trail. The Cascade Mountains may not be the tallest or the oldest of their kind, but they still have many beautiful waterfalls to charm visitors. Portland, though a thriving urban environment, is also the only city to have a volcano within its city limits. Perhaps all of the natural beauty surrounding Oregon residents is what inspired them to care so much about preserving the Earth's resources: The state passed laws protecting its land and water even before the rest of the country wised up about the importance of taking care of the environment.

How Oregon Got Its Name

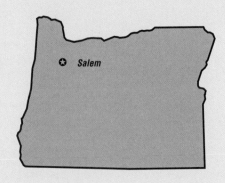

Several different theories exist to explain how Oregon was named. One idea is that the name comes from the French Canadian word *ouragain,* meaning "hurricane," or "storm," in reference to the stormy Columbia River. Another opinion is that the name was derived from the Spanish word *orejon,* meaning "big ear," which would have been meant to describe the Indian peoples in the region. Lastly, the name could have been born from the Spanish word *oregano,* meaning "wild sage," since the plant is common to the area. At least Oregon's nicknames are known for certain— the state is called the Beaver State, the Web Foot State, the Sunset State, the Valentine State, and the Hard-Case State.

Historic Site

✪ Million Hill Village, Salem

State Trivia

✪ Are you a whiz with a sand castle? There's an annual contest at Canon Beach to build the best one.

✪ Portland was actually named from a coin toss. Francis Pettygrove from Portland, Maine, wanted to name the city after his hometown—and so did Amos Lovejoy of Boston. Guess we don't have to tell you who won!

✪ Oregon has more ghost towns than any other state. Spooky . . .

✪ The only state flag to carry two separate designs, Oregon's flag shows a beaver on the reverse side.

WORD SCRAMBLE

zmaama _____

adcasec _____

rnmotevinen _____

avrebe _____

goptyetver _____

aequl _____

lscrpenuaeh _____

ltprdnao _____

❂ If you're a windsurfing fan, you should definitely visit the Columbia River Gorge—it's considered by many to be the best spot in the world for the sport!

❂ Bet you never heard about this one: The world's smallest park, located in Portland, was created on St. Patrick's Day for leprechauns and snail races. The park totals a mere 452 inches!

❂ Another forward-thinking move from this ahead-of-its-time state. In 1955, Oregon mandated that women should receive equal pay for equal work. (Sounds so logical, doesn't it?)

❂ Cowabunga! Matt Groening, the creator of The Simpsons, was born in Portland.

CROSSWORD

Across

1. Portland has one in its city limits!
2. ____ River Gorge
5. Matt ____, Simpsons creator
6. Build a ____ castle at Canon Beach

Down

1. Because it was inducted on February 14th, Oregon is called the ____ State.
2. ____ Lake
3. Oregon's state tree (two words)
5. Oregon has the longest overland pioneer ___.

Pennsylvania

DATE OF STATEHOOD:
December 12, 1787

STATE CAPITAL: Harrisburg

STATE TREE: Hemlock

STATE FLOWER: Mountain laurel

STATE BIRD: Ruffed grouse

A state where both the Declaration of Independence and U.S. Constitution were written was destined to be key to the history of America. The famous Liberty Bell was first rung in Independence Hall in Philadelphia on July 8, 1776, after the first public reading of the Declaration of Independence. What's the truth about the crack? No one knows for sure, but the bell, now on display at Independence National Historic Park, supposedly cracked after being rung for the death of Supreme Court Chief Justice John Marshall. Philadelphia also has several significant houses on its land: the first presidential mansion, and the Betsy Ross House, once the home of seamstress Elizabeth Griscom Ross, who according to legend made the first American flag. Outside of Philadelphia, the town of Gettysburg gained fame as the site of the battle that turned the tide of the Civil War, leading to the North's victory. And President Lincoln delivered his well-known Gettysburg Address there on November 19, 1863.

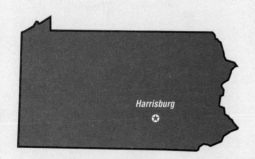

Harrisburg

WORD SEARCH

```
G R O U N D H O G W T B F W O U T A U B
A Y E A S T X Q T F R W O R G A Z K P H
C H I S R J R M Y I Z D J T D I A V H K
F V N J N Y A I N A V L Y S L G E S I D
D A D G V T W D W B C O D U A S U B L U
E R E R O F O I Y K Q L M N A K I R A F
N N P M X N O I T U T I T S N O C N D U
O G E J T B V K A B L T B I O L H R E G
T O N I K V D W L C O U F C R E P D L C
S E D U A L C X B U N C D A K P B J P O
Y W E F B L P C T W H N H A D H K L H F
E D N S M P O W R E K A G H E B E P I S
K O C T A C H J O U I M R K N C I P A M
K C E U L D T Q S G X R W R W F J A R L
G R B P L T Q X S H A Z B E I M G V D J
B N H D T E M W E P Y N F C O S S C O V
L T R O O R P S G U E W K M Z D B I V A
M P C E V B U R G N S V E N J V O U K R
O L K U P G S Q H J V M S I G N R S R Y
A L G H M N M A G A Z I N E H O G W I G
```

WORDS
Alcott
Constitution

Groundhog
Harrisburg
Independence

Keystone
Magazine
Philadelphia

Ross
Sylvania

How Pennsylvania Got Its Name

When William Penn founded the colony, he wanted to call it *Sylvania*, Latin for "woods" or "woodland." But King Charles II wanted to name the land for Penn himself. The compromise, Pennsylvania, means "Penn's woods." The state is also called the Keystone State and the Quaker State.

President Born Here!

✪ James Buchanan, 15th president

Historic Sites

✪ Valley Forge National Historical Park

✪ Gettysburg National Military Park

State Trivia

✪ Hershey Park, the chocolate-themed amusement park, can be found in the town of Hershey—which is also home to the largest chocolate factory in the world. They hold an annual chocolate festival in February. Yum!

✪ Pennsylvania had the first fire department *and* the first hospital. They were certainly on top of things!

✪ Since 1946, the Little League World Series has been held at Williamsport every August.

✪ In Pennsylvania Dutch Country, the Amish community live in almost complete isolation from their neighbors, preserving their traditions of living without the aid of modern conveniences such as electricity or cars. Impressive!

✪ American's first magazine, called—surprise—*American Magazine*, was published for just three months in 1741.

✪ William Penn might be happy to know that his "woods" have made the state one of the leading growers of Christmas trees!

✪ *Little Women* author Louisa May Alcott is a Pennsylvania native.

✪ Every February on Groundhog Day, people flock to Punxsutawney to see if little Punxsutawney Phil—the most famous groundhog in the world—sees his shadow or not. Supposedly, the answer to this question reveals how much longer winter will last!

CROSSWORD

Across

2. Little _____ World Series
4. 15th president, James ___
7. Chocolate town
8. Punxsutawney _____

Down

1. Betsy Ross's creation
2. Site of battle in Civil War
5. The _____ people lived in Pennsylvania Dutch Country
6. Liberty _____

Rhode Island

DATE OF STATEHOOD:
May 29, 1790

STATE CAPITAL: Providence

STATE TREE: Red maple

STATE FLOWER: Violet

STATE BIRD: Rhode Island red chicken

Rhode Island, the last of the original thirteen colonies to become a state, was founded by Roger Williams on the basic ideal of religious freedom. So it's not surprising that both the oldest church—First Baptist Church, built in 1639 in Providence—and the oldest synagogue—Touro Synagogue, built in 1763 in Newport—are located in this state. More artifacts? Portsmouth has the oldest schoolhouse, and the White Horse Tavern in Newport is the oldest operating tavern in the United States.

How Rhode Island Got Its Name

Some say that the name comes from the Dutch *roodt eylandt,* meaning "red island," in reference to its red clay shores. Another explanation is that the Italian explorer Giovanni da Verrazano was comparing nearby Block Island to the Mediterranean Island of Rhodes. Rhode Island has a number of nicknames: Little Rhody, the Smallest State, the Land of Roger Williams, the Plantation State, and the Ocean State.

Historic Site

- ✪ Slater Mill Historic Museum, Pawtucket—one of the first textile mills in North America

State Trivia

- ✪ Although it's the smallest state, Rhode Island has the longest official name: the State of Rhode Island and Providence Plantations.

- ✪ The first British troops sent from England to stop America's revolution landed in Newport, where we're guessing they didn't receive a very warm welcome!

- ✪ Newport is also home to the International Tennis Hall of Fame, nestled between shops and restaurants on a quaint city block.

- ✪ George M. Cohan, composer of "I'm a Yankee Doodle Dandy," was born in Providence in 1878.

- ✪ For several centuries, Rhode Island had five capitals at once. Then, for a short time, it had two. Providence finally became the only capital in 1900.

- ✪ Residents celebrate their own Independence Day on May 4—the day the colony declared independence from England!

South Carolina

DATE OF STATEHOOD:
May 23, 1788

STATE CAPITAL: Columbia

STATE TREE: Palmetto

STATE FLOWER: Yellow jessamine

STATE BIRD: Carolina wren

The state in which the most Revolutionary War battles were fought is also the state where the first shots of the Civil War were fired: at Fort Sumter, on April 12, 1861. Despite the bloody history, South Carolina is still full of beautiful scenery, like the 18th- and 19th-century mansions in Charleston, and the famous cypress and magnolia gardens—including the Middleton Place Gardens, the oldest in America.

How South Carolina Got Its Name

Like its northern counterpart, South Carolina was named first to honor King Charles IX of France, and then for King Charles I and II of England. However, the state does have its own nicknames, and they include the Rice State, the Swamp State, the Keystone of the South Atlantic Seaboard, the Iodine State, and the Palmetto State.

President Born Here!

✪ Andrew Jackson, 7th president

Historic Sites

✪ Historic District, Cheraw

✪ Andrew Jackson State Park, near Lancaster—birthplace of the president

State Trivia

✪ Never think your vote can't make a difference! On November 2, 1954, Strom Thurmond received 139,106 write-in votes for the senate race, enough to make him the first U.S. senator elected by write-in vote.

✪ South Carolina is responsible for the first steam-engine locomotive and the first public museum.

✪ The official state amphibian is the salamander, and the state dance is the Shag. (Now just imagine the combination of those two . . .)

✪ Why the Palmetto State? The first battle of the Revolutionary war was won by South Carolina soldiers from a fort built of palmetto logs—Fort Moultrie on Sullivan's Island.

✪ Before you can make it to "The Show," you usually have to prove yourself in the minors. Minor league baseball players have been warming up in South Carolina for years—the Duncan Park baseball stadium in Spartanburg is the oldest minor league stadium in the nation!

South Dakota

DATE OF STATEHOOD:
November 2, 1889

STATE CAPITAL: Pierre

STATE TREE: Black Hills spruce

STATE FLOWER: American pasque flower

STATE BIRD: Ring-necked pheasant

South Dakota is known for its number and variety of monuments and memorials. Most famous is the Mount Rushmore National Monument, where sculptor Gutzon Borglum carved the faces of Presidents George Washington, Thomas Jefferson, Abraham Lincoln and Theodore Roosevelt into the granite cliff. Borglum died before finishing the sculpture, but his son completed the work. Also worth seeing is the Crazy Horse Memorial—another mountain carving, in honor of the Dakota Indian leader. And Jewel Cave National Monument is full of beautiful crystals!

How South Dakota Got Its Name

Like North Dakota, the state was named for the Dakota Indian word meaning "friends," or "allies." South Dakota is also called the Sunshine State, the Coyote State, the Blizzard State, and the Artesian State.

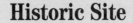

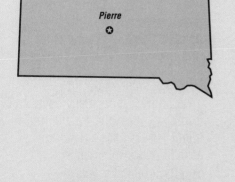

Pierre

Historic Site

✪ Mount Rushmore National Monument

State Trivia

✪ The town of De Smet was the setting for *Little Town on the Prairie* and five other beloved Laura Ingalls Wilder books. Her parents were the first white settlers in the area when they moved there in 1879.

✪ Clark is home to a mashed potato wrestling contest. (Do you think they use butter and sour cream, too?)

✪ Feeling lucky? In the Black Hills, people can still pan for gold today!

✪ South Dakota natives must have the fighting spirit in their blood. A couple examples? Tough frontierswoman Calamity Jane and the well known American frontier marshal Wild Bill Hickok were both born in the Coyote State. Hickok also died there—he was shot during a poker game!

Tennessee

DATE OF STATEHOOD:
June 1, 1796

STATE CAPITAL: Nashville

STATE TREE: Tulip poplar

STATE FLOWER: Iris

STATE BIRD: Mockingbird

Tennessee earned its nickname, the Volunteer State, during the War of 1812 when volunteer soldiers turned out in droves to help in the Battle of New Orleans. The state later became the last to secede from the Union during the Civil War—but also the first to be readmitted after the war ended! Its split loyalties are reflected by the monument in Greeneville that honors both the Union *and* Confederate armies—the only one of its kind in the country.

Nashville

How Tennessee Got Its Name

The Cherokee Indians gave the name *tanasi* to two villages on the Little Tennessee River, and the name *Tennessee* later came from this word. However, no one is certain of the actual meaning of *tanasi*. The state is also known as the Volunteer State, the Big Bend State, the Hog State, the Hominy State, and the Mother of Southwestern Statesmen.

State Trivia:

✪ Nashville is the heart of country music, and Memphis is home to Graceland, Elvis Presley's home and gravesite.

✪ Reelfoot Lake, in the northwest corner of Tennessee, was formed by the New Madrid earthquakes of 1811–12. The lake has so many turtles that it's now called the Turtle Capital of the World. (Bet you didn't even know there *was* one of those!)

✪ In Craighead Cavern you can find the world's largest underground lake: the Lost Sea.

✪ The great American frontier hero Davy Crockett, who died defending the Alamo in Texas, was born in the Great Smoky Mountains in 1786.

✪ There are more than 3,800 *known* caves in Tennessee. Feel like exploring?

✪ The National Civil Rights Museum was constructed in the Lorraine Motel in Memphis to memorialize Reverend Martin Luther King, Jr., who was assassinated here.

Texas

DATE OF STATEHOOD:
December 29, 1845

STATE CAPITAL: Austin

STATE TREE: Pecan

STATE FLOWER: Bluebonnet

STATE BIRD: Mockingbird

Second only to Alaska in size, Texas has also had the flags of six different nations fly over it: Spain, France, Mexico, the Republic of Texas, the Confederate States, and—of course—the United States. Its varied background shows in its many different features. It has the biggest ranch in the country, King Ranch, which is larger than the entire state of Rhode Island! The National Cowgirl Hall of Fame is in Texas, along with the Texas Rangers Hall of Fame. Texas is a leader in industry, too. It's home to NASA's Johnson Space Center in Houston, and has been nicknamed the Silicon Valley of the South, since big name computer companies Dell and Compaq set up shop there.

How Texas Got Its Name

The name comes from the Caddo Indian word *teysha,* meaning "hello friend," or "friendship," which was used by the Spanish to refer to friendly tribes. Texas is also called the Lone Star State, the Beef State, and the Banner State.

Austin

Presidents Born Here!

✪ Dwight D. Eisenhower, 34th president

✪ Lyndon B. Johnson, 36th president

Historic Site

✪ The Alamo, San Antonio

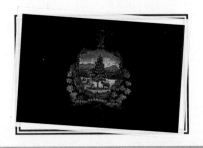

State Trivia

✪ Does Batman know? More species of bats live in Texas than in any other part of the United States, and the biggest urban bat colony can be found in Austin.

✪ The Astrodome, named in honor of Houston's contributions to the space program, was the first covered baseball stadium. Completed in 1965, the climate-controlled stadium had one big problem—natural grass wouldn't grow under the fake light from above. And so, inventors created a new green carpet product made to resemble grass as closely as possible. Yep—that's how Astroturf was born!

CROSSWORD

Across

2. Covered baseball stadium
4. Texas has two different types of _____
5. 36th president, Lyndon _____
6. Texas landmark (two words)

Down

1. Night creatures of Texas
2. "Remember the _____"
3. 34th president, Dwight _____
4. National _____ Hall of Fame

✪ Mollie Bailey became the first woman to manage a circus with her Mollie A. Bailey Show in Texas in the late nineteenth century.

✪ Although residents along the Gulf Coast live in a subtropical climate, it actually gets very cold in the northern part of Texas.

✪ A state that knows how to party! Every October, Dallas hosts the biggest state fair in the country.

✪ Ever heard the saying, "Remember the Alamo?" In 1836, 187 Texas volunteer soldiers held out against Mexican soldiers at the fort known as the Alamo for 13 days. They were all eventually killed, but Sam Houston, another Texas leader, used the cry, "Remember the Alamo!" to inspire the rest of his troops, who later won independence for the state.

✪ The Tyler Municipal Rose Garden is the world's largest rose garden.

MAZE

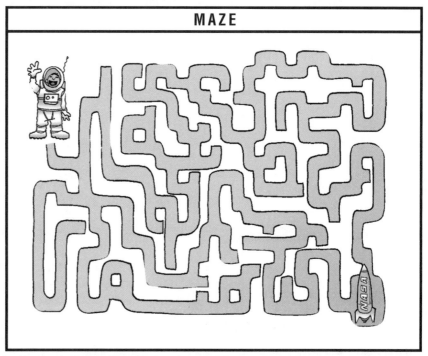

Utah

DATE OF STATEHOOD:
January 4, 1896

STATE CAPITAL: Salt Lake City

STATE TREE: Blue spruce

STATE FLOWER: Sego lily

STATE BIRD: Seagull

Salt Lake City

Utah has a magical mix of vast deserts and beautiful mountains, but it is best known for the Great Salt Lake Desert, and the famous lake for which the desert was named. Water can flow into the Great Salt Lake, but it can't drain out. So instead, the water simply evaporates into the clean, clear air. The stunning Uinta mountains make up the only significant east-west mountain range in the country, and in southeastern Utah, the famous "four corners" spot (where four states intermeet) allows visitors to glimpse neighbor states Colorado, New Mexico, and Arizona at once. Pretty cool!

How Utah Got Its Name

The name is derived from the White Mountain Apache word *yuttahih,* meaning "one who is higher up," or "people of the mountains." The Apaches were actually describing the Navajo, but Europeans mistakenly believed the name was being used in reference to the Utes, and so the state became Utah. Its nicknames include the Beehive State, the Mormon State, the Salt Lake State, and the Land of the Saints.

State Trivia

- ✪ Kanab is known as Utah's "Little Hollywood" because so many movies are filmed in the area, and the Hollywood Stuntmen's Hall of Fame is actually located here in Moab.

- ✪ Rainbow Bridge, the largest natural stone bridge in the world, stretches 275 feet across and reaches 290 feet high!

- ✪ Robert Le Roy Parker was born in Beaver on April 15, 1866. Never heard of him? You probably know him by the name he gave himself when he got older—Butch Cassidy. Together with the other outlaws that made up the Wild Bunch, Cassidy organized the longest string of successful bank robberies in American history in the Old West!

- ✪ The Great Salt Lake isn't the only important body of water in Utah! The Escalante River is considered the last major river to be discovered in the contiguous United States.

- ✪ Check out the Dinosaur National Monument near Vernal—it has real dinosaur fossils!

- ✪ The water in the Great Salt Lake is significantly saltier than any ocean. In fact, the only water with a higher salt content is found in the Dead Sea!

Vermont

DATE OF STATEHOOD:
March 4, 1791

STATE CAPITAL: Montpelier

STATE TREE: Sugar maple

STATE FLOWER: Red clover

STATE BIRD: Hermit thrush

Truly a *sweet* state, Vermont is both the largest producer of maple syrup in the United States *and* the original home to Ben & Jerry's ice cream. Skiers delight in the nine-month-long ski season; lasting from October to June, it's the longest in the country! The state's capital, Montpelier, may be the smallest in the country, but Vermont was the first state admitted to the Union after the thirteen original colonies—and one of its natives, Calvin Coolidge, was destined to be a patriot—he was born on the fourth of July!

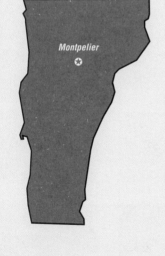

How Vermont Got Its Name

The name, given to the region by Samuel de Champlain in 1647, comes from the French words *verd* and *mont,* meaning "green mountain" in 17th-Century French spelling. Vermont's nickname isn't too far from its actual name—it's called the Green Mountain State.

Presidents Born Here!

✪ Chester Alan Arthur, 21st president

✪ Calvin Coolidge, 30th president

Historic Sites

✪ Candle Mill Village, Arlington

✪ Peter Matteson Tavern, Shaftsbury—200-year-old stagecoach tavern

✪ Hyde Log Cabin, Grand Isle— built in 1738

State Trivia

✪ The Haskell Opera House, which rests on the Derby Line, provides its patrons with quite a cultural experience. Because of its unique location, the audience sits in the United States while the performers they are watching are technically in Canada!

✪ Vermont's Green Mountains, for which the state was named, are nearly half a billion years old—among the oldest in the country.

✪ Got gephyrophobia (fear of crossing bridges)? Then beware: Vermont has over a hundred covered bridges.

✪ Why wasn't Vermont one of the original colonies to enter the Union? Neither New York nor New Hampshire was willing to acknowledge Vermont as a separate colony. With no other choice, Vermont declared its *own* independence from Britain in 1777, calling itself the nation of New Connecticut. Once New York and New Hampshire worked out their land claims, Vermont was able to become the fourteenth colony. But you have to admire the state's determination!

Virginia

DATE OF STATEHOOD:
June 25, 1788

STATE CAPITAL: Richmond

STATE TREE: Dogwood

STATE FLOWER: Dogwood

STATE BIRD: Cardinal

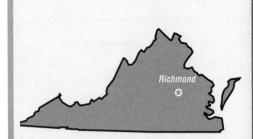

It is simply not possible to over-exaggerate Virginia's huge role in this country's history. Jamestown, the state's first capital, was also the first English settlement in the United States. Four of the first five presidents were born here, along with *another* four presidents and six first ladies! The war that gave us our independence—the American Revolution—ended in Yorktown with the surrender of Cornwallis. It was in Richmond that politician Patrick Henry uttered the impassioned words, "Give me liberty or give me death!"

CROSSWORD

Across

4. Virginian Mother of _____
6. Washington's home, Mt. _____
7. _____ Valley
8. Where Cornwallis surrendered

Down

1. Unknown _____, buried in Arlington
2. Turkey Day
3. Colonial _____
5. Thomas Jefferson's home

How Virginia Got Its Name

The state was named for Queen Elizabeth I of England, who was known as the Virgin Queen. Virginia's nicknames include the Old Dominion, the Mother of Presidents, the Mother of States, the Mother of Statesmen, and the Cavalier State.

Presidents Born Here!

✪ George Washington, 1st president

✪ Thomas Jefferson, 3rd president

✪ James Madison, 4th president

✪ James Monroe, 5th president

✪ William Henry Harrison, 9th president

✪ John Tyler, 10th president

✪ Zachary Tayler, 12th president

✪ Woodrow Wilson, 28th president

Historic Sites

✪ Jamestown, with replicas of a 1607 fort and the ships that carried settlers to America

✪ Colonial Williamsburg

State Trivia

✪ Mount Vernon, George Washington's home, and Monticello, the house Jefferson designed himself, are both open to visitors today.

✪ There are plenty of monuments in our country to the first president, but the only full-length statue of George Washington was placed in the capitol in Richmond in 1796.

✪ Skyline Drive, a 105-mile scenic highway along the crest of the Blue Ridge Mountains, offers incredible view of the Shenandoah Valley to the west and the Piedmont Plateau to the east.

✪ Thousands of American soldiers are buried in Arlington National Cemetery, where the Tomb of the Unknowns can also be found. This tomb holds soldiers whose identities were never learned—but represent the many who have given their lives for the country.

✪ Forget time travel machines—there's an easier way to go back to the past. Colonial Williamsburg is a living recreation of a colonial village, with houses, stores, taverns, streets, and buildings made to look exactly as they did when George Washington and Thomas Jefferson traveled through here in the 1700s.

✪ America's Bill of Rights was modeled after Virginia's own version of the document. What a trendsetting state!

MAZE

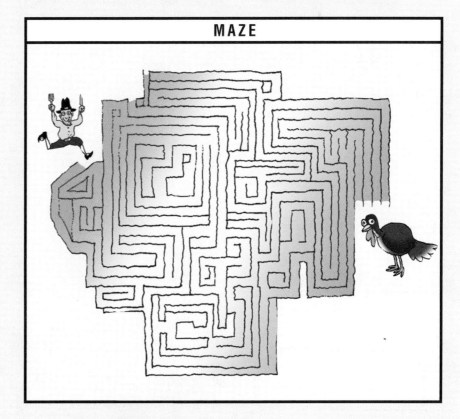

Washington

DATE OF STATEHOOD: November 11, 1889

STATE CAPITAL: Olympia

STATE TREE: Western hemlock

STATE FLOWER: Pink rhododendron

STATE BIRD: Willow goldfinch

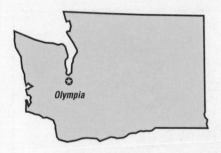

Olympia

Talk about a high-reaching state! Built for the 1962 World's fair, Seattle's famous Space Needle is a full 607 feet high, with a revolving restaurant and observation deck at the top so visitors can enjoy the view. The 105-foot-tall Tacoma Totem Pole, carved from a single cedar tree in 1903, is one of the tallest remaining totem poles in the world. And the volcanic peak Mount Rainier, the highest mountain in the state, is capped with the largest glacier in the United States. Washington's residents' achievements are just as lofty as the state's natural wonders and human-made structures. Workers at the Boeing 741 plant in Everett (the world's largest building!) make aircraft and spacecraft—including the Lunar Rover, the vehicle astronauts use to travel on the moon. And Bill Gates, the entrepreneur who shot up the business ladder in a flash, has his Microsoft headquarters in Redmond.

How Washington Got Its Name

Washington was originally the Territory of Columbia, but since America already had a District of Columbia, the state was named after the country's first president, George Washington. Washington is also known as the Evergreen State and the Chinook State.

Historic Sites

✪ Fort Vancouver National Historic Site

✪ Klondike Gold Rush National Historical Park/Pioneer Park, Seattle

State Trivia

✪ Starbucks, the gourmet coffeehouse that can now be found just about everywhere, first opened in Seattle in 1981.

✪ The cloudiest and snowiest towns in the U.S. are both in Washington. Quillayute has about 241 cloudy days a year, while Stampede Pass gets an average of 431.9 inches of snow annually.

✪ The oldest operating gas station in the U.S. still pumps gas in Zilla.

✪ Mount St. Helens volcano last erupted in 1980—so don't get too close!

WORD SCRAMBLE

aecps denlee _____

paelps _____

ssktuabcr _____

libl agset _____

knip ohdrnnordedo _____

aulnr reorv _____

tetmo olep _____

noumt iarienr _____

✪ Every year on the second Sunday in June, citizens from America and Canada gather in the city of Blaine. The reason? To pay tribute to the Peace Arch, a monument built there to symbolize the friendship between the two countries.

✪ The Ginkgo Petrified Forest State Park is known as the largest of only three petrified forests in the world. What's so special about a petrified forest? This one has over 200 species of fossilized stone trees. The trees were once entombed by primeval lava flows, then preserved over the years by bizarre chemical reactions. Cool, huh?

✪ Now that's weird! The only state to be named for an American president *also* has a famous landmark named for a British soldier! Peter Rainier fought against Americans in the Revolutionary War before having a volcanic peak here carry his name.

✪ Keep the doctor away! Washington is the world's leading apple grower.

✪ Bob Barker, the host of the long-running television game show *The Price is Right,* was born in Darrington.

✪ The Olympia Dairy Queen was the proud owner of the first soft-serve ice cream machine. There's a treat that caught on fast!

✪ Icy! Washington has more glaciers than the other 47 contiguous states put together.

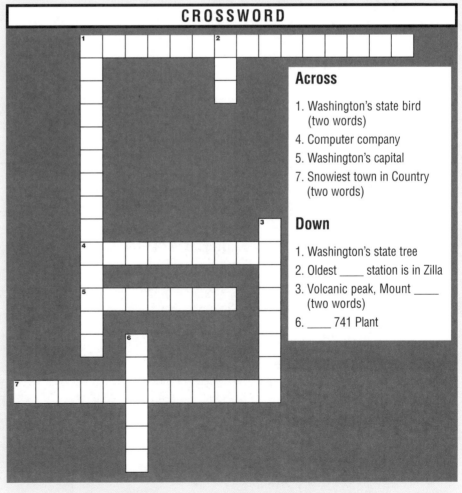

CROSSWORD

Across

1. Washington's state bird (two words)
4. Computer company
5. Washington's capital
7. Snowiest town in Country (two words)

Down

1. Washington's state tree
2. Oldest _____ station is in Zilla
3. Volcanic peak, Mount _____ (two words)
6. _____ 741 Plant

West Virginia

DATE OF STATEHOOD:
June 20, 1863

STATE CAPITAL: Charleston

STATE TREE: Sugar maple

STATE FLOWER: Big rhododendron

STATE BIRD: Cardinal

West Virginia has the unique distinction of being the only state to receive the official right to call itself that by a presidential proclamation! Lincoln designated West Virginia a state in 1863, after the residents insisted on seceding from Virginia in 1861—without its permission—due to conflicts over several issues. Most significantly, West Virginians were opposed to Virginia's decision to fight for the Confederacy in the Civil War. Devoted to the Union, West Virginia saw one of its natives—Baily Thornsberry Brown—become the first Union soldier killed in the war.

How West Virginia Got Its Name

The name's derivation is the same as that of the state it was born from: Virginia. West Virginia is also called the Mountain State, the Switzerland of America (popular nickname, isn't it!), and the Panhandle State.

Historic Sites

✪ Watters Smith Memorial Park—200-year-old pioneer farm

✪ West Virginia State Farm Museum, Point Pleasant

Charleston

State Trivia

✪ Harpers Ferry National Historic Park commemorates the passionate abolitionist John Brown's attack on an armory here in 1859. Brown, along with twenty-seven other men, raided the armory to steal weapons for their cause. However, the effort was unsuccessful in helping to end slavery, and Brown was later executed for his actions.

✪ Olympic-medal-winning gymnast Mary Lou Retton is a West Virginia native.

✪ The nation's first Mother's Day was celebrated in Grafton on May 10, 1908. President Wilson later proclaimed the day be observed nationwide, and Grafton now has an International Shrine to Motherhood!

✪ The Green Bank National Radio Astronomy Observatory is the first major radio observatory built in the country. Workers here have listened to radio waves from space since 1958!

✪ Lost your marbles? Stop by Parkersburg, where most of the country's glass marbles are made!

Wisconsin

DATE OF STATEHOOD:
May 29, 1848

STATE CAPITAL: Madison

STATE TREE: Sugar maple

STATE FLOWER: Wood violet

STATE BIRD: Robin

Cheese, please? Wisconsin is most widely known for its leading role in the production of dairy products. The state provides 40 percent of the nation's cheese, and 20 percent of our butter. Mmm! But aside from being responsible for these tasty treats, Wisconsin has also played a big role in our society's intellectual growth. The country's original kindergarten was founded in Watertown in 1856 by Margarethe Meyer Schurz. The first minimum wage requirement was also instituted here, along with the first worker's compensation and pensions, teachers' pensions, mothers' pensions, old age pensions, and unemployment insurance.

How Wisconsin Got Its Name

There is some controversy over the name, but one theory is that it comes from a Chippewa word that means "grassy place," which would refer to the area around the Wisconsin River. The state is also known as the Badger State and the Copper State.

Historic Sites

✪ Cave of the Mounds, near Blue Mounds

✪ Stonefield Village, near Cassville

✪ Galloway House and Village, Fond du Lac

✪ Historical Society Log Village and Museum, Reedsburg

State Trivia

✪ Since the state is almost completely surrounded by water, it makes sense that the town of Wisconsin Dells would have a water-themed park called Noah's Ark.

✪ The Circus World Museum in Baraboo was built to honor the place where the Ringling Brothers Circus began in 1882.

✪ Author Laura Ingalls Wilder and architect Frank Lloyd Wright were both born in Wisconsin. Golda Meir—the woman who later became the Prime Minister of Israel at the age of seventy— grew up in Milwaukee.

✪ The first practical typewriter was designed in Milwaukee in 1867, and it was probably a lot more welcome than the first state income tax, which started in Wisconsin in 1911.

✪ Burgers and bikes! Seymour is home to the Hamburger Hall of Fame, while Milwaukee is the home of Harley Davidson Motorcycles.

Wyoming

DATE OF STATEHOOD:
July 10, 1890

STATE CAPITAL: Cheyenne

STATE TREE: Plains cottonwood

STATE FLOWER: Indian paintbrush

STATE BIRD: Western meadowlark

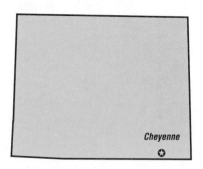

It's rather surprising that Wyoming is the least populous state, considering all the beauty and intrigue the state has to offer. Yellowstone National Park was designated the first National Park in 1872, and the Devils Tower National Monument became the country's first national monument in 1906, before later being featured in director Steven Spielberg's popular movie, *Close Encounters of the Third Kind*. The Old Faithful geyser erupts about once an hour—an awesome sight—and visitors can also check out Medicine Wheel, a prehistoric stone construction resembling a huge wheel that's believed to be somewhere around *2000* years old!

How Wyoming Got Its Name

The name comes from the word *mecheweaming,* which has two different meanings; in the Delaware Indian language it means "mountains and valleys alternating," but in Algonquin it translates as "large prairie place." Wyoming is also called the Equality State, the Big Wyoming, and the Cowboy State.

Historic Sites

- Buffalo Bill Historical Center, Cody
- Plains Indian Museum, Cody
- Fort Laramie National Historic Site
- South Pass City, Lander—gold camp near the Oregon trail

State Trivia

- Cody is known as the Rodeo Capital of the World.

- Outlaw Butch Cassidy was confined at one point in the jail at Wyoming Territorial Prison Park, in Laramie.

- In 1869, before it was even a state, Wyoming earned its nickname as The Equality State when it became the first American location to count women's votes. The first female governor also took office in this state—Nellie Tayloe Ross was elected in 1924.

- The once-mysterious hot spots of land in Yellowstone National Park are actually caused by molten rock that collected close to the Earth's surface. Basically, this is not a prime place to go digging!

Learn More and Play More—on the World Wide Web

The Web is a terrific resource for just about anything. Did you know that there are sites just about coin collecting? And still more sites where you can learn additional facts about the states? Hey there are even sites where you can play games and have fun while learning more about coin collecting and the states they represent! So check it out!!!

COIN COLLECTING SITES

United States Mint 50 State Quarters™ Program

http://www.usmint.gov/50states/default.cfm

Includes an online catalog and information on release dates, coin production, and the new golden dollar!

Coin Collecting FAQ

http://www.telesphere.com/ts/coins/faq.html

Areas include:
- What's it worth?
- What coins do people collect?
- What's the best way to get started?
- How do you handle coins?

And much more!

The United States Mint: H.I.P. Pocket Change It's History in Your Pocket

http://www.usmint.gov/kids/

An amazing site, with areas for teachers and kids alike! There is a coin of the month feature and sections with fun and games. The Time Machine will take you back in history to visit all the great people and places that you'll find associated with coins.

FUN TRIVIA

United States History: State Trivia

http://www.usahistory.com/trivia/

Features include a bulletin board, historical trivia, and state trivia.

United States Presidents Trivia

http://www.synnergy.com/day/prestc.htm#tca

Features include a trivia quiz, a bibliography, a place to ask questions, homework helper pages and a handy search engine to the site.

The Trivia Portal

http://www.funtrivia.com/

Among the many categories of trivia, you will find areas on geography, history, and politics.

Answer Key

Alaska, pages 6–7

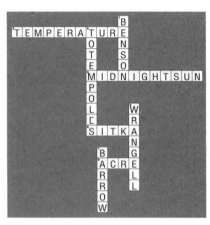

Colorado, pages 12–13

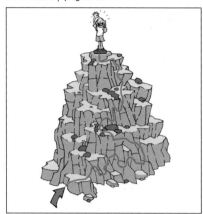

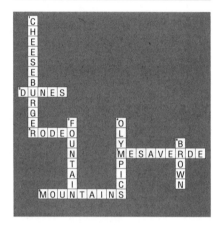

Idaho, pages 20–21

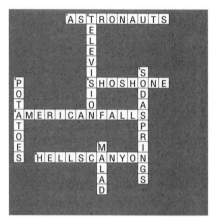

California, pages 10–11

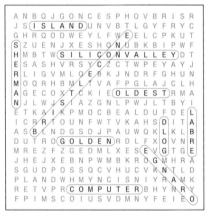

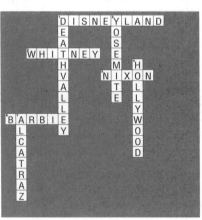

Florida, pages 16–17

WORD SCRAMBLE

neyisd = Disney

redsavegle = Everglades

asnilpneu = eninsula

seyk = keys

heusnisn = sunshine

mgrartsno = Armstrong

lcvanaaer = Canaveral

tedaroag = Gatorade

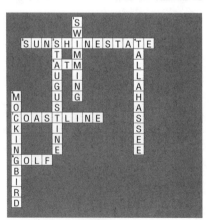

Illinois, pages 22–23

Indiana, pages 24–25

V I C E P R E S I D E N T S
with crossword including BASEBALL, ROBBERY, BIRD, LAWN, SANTACLAUS, AUTO, FOOTBALL

Louisiana, page 30

Massachusetts, pages 34–35

WORD SCRAMBLE

vhdrara = Harvard

siterwr = writers

mypluoht korc = Plymouth Rock

tebkalbals = basketball

nbtsoo eat ptray = Boston Tea Party

olylvellabl = volleyball

igf wtenno = fig newton

lupa ervere = Paul Revere

Maryland, pages 32–33

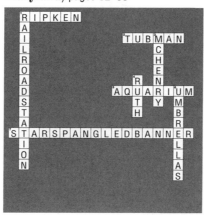

Crossword including RIPKEN, TUBMAN, CHENEY, RAILROADSTATION, RUTH, AQUARIUM, UMBRELLAS, STARSPANGLEDBANNER

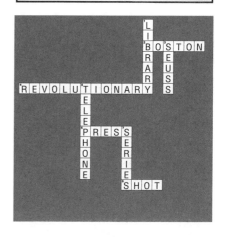

Crossword including LIBRARY, BOSTON, SEUSS, REVOLUTIONARY, TELEPHONE, PRESS, SERIES, SHOT

Kentucky, pages 28–29

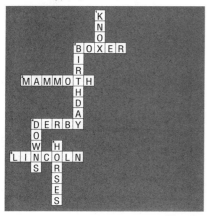

Crossword including KNOX, BOXER, BIRTHDAY, MAMMOTH, DERBY, DOWNS, LINCOLN, HORSES

WORD SCRAMBLE

neixnglot = Lexington

orghotrdbheu = Thoroughbred

sbeuslarg = bluegrass

bnroic = Corbin

oneob = Boone

bcacoot = tobacco

ogdndoler = goldenrod

fotfrrkna = Frankfort

NOTE:
There are other solutions possible to the mazes on pages 24, 33, and 37.

Michigan, pages 36–37

Crossword including MAGIC, MOTOWN, GREATLAKES, AUTOMOBILES, DETROITZOO, GINGERALE, FORD, CEREAL

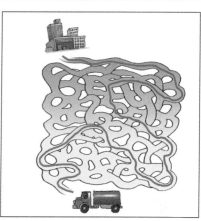

Answer Key continued

New Hampshire, pages 44–45

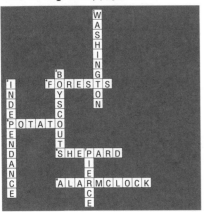

WORD SCRAMBLE

mripray = primary

ihtnn = ninth

focnraina = Franconia

rtnaieg = granite

msrtopouht = Portsmouth

engheontse = Stonehenge

omsna = Mason

cnoorcd = Concord

New Mexico, pages 48–49

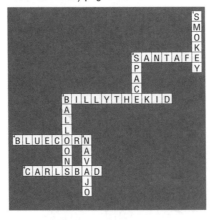

Oregon, pages 56–57

WORD SCRAMBLE

zmaama = Mazama

adcasec = cascade

rnmotevinen = environment

avrebe = beaver

goptyetver = Pettygrove

aequl = equal

lscrpenuaeh = leprechauns

ltprdnao = Portland

New Jersey, pages 46–47

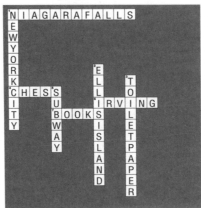

WORD SCRAMBLE

wbdraklao = boardwalk

ebsalabl = baseball

msis mreaiac = Miss America

dneois = Edison

csalmlpeb = Campbells

tnsieien = Einstein

edinsr = diners

oby ctsuos = Boy Scouts

New York, pages 50–51

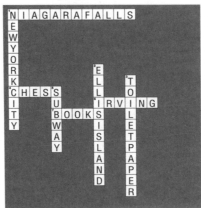

Pennsylvania, pages 58–59

78

Texas, pages 64–65

Washington, pages 70–71

WORD SCRAMBLE

aecps denlee = space needle

paelps = apples

ssktuabcr = Starbucks

libl agset = Bill Gates

knip ohdrnnordedo = pink rhododendron

aulnr reorv = lunar rover

tetmo olep = totem pole

noumt iarienr = Mount Rainier

Virginia, pages 68–69

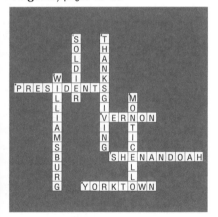

NOTE:
There are other solutions possible to the mazes on pages 49 and 65.

Editor: Michael Cavanaugh
Art Director: Jeff Batzli
Designer: Gina Rossi
Photography Editor: Lori Epstein
Digital Imaging: Daniel J. Rutkowski

Illustrations:
State Bird, Flowers: Ernest O. Brown, ©White Mountain Puzzles, Jackson, NH
Trivia: ©Karen Stormer Brooks
Mazes: Daniel Lish
Word Games: Paul Taurins
Maps: Steve Arcella

ISBN 0760723451

2000 Friedman/Fairfax Publishers

Printed in the United States

00 01 02 M 9 8 7 6 5 4 3 2 1